ANEAN

INDIAN
OCEAN

SOUTH
PACIFIC
OCEAN

RIDDLES OF MANY LANDS

Riddles of

many Lands

BY **CARL WITHERS** AND **SULA BENET**

ILLUSTRATED BY **LILI CASSEL**

 ABELARD-SCHUMAN NEW YORK

CONTENTS

ABOUT THIS BOOK

Riddles of Many Lands is designed to entertain young-sters and grownups alike with a generous sampling of riddles from around the world. It contains eight hundred riddles from over ninety countries, regions and tribal or ethnic groups, representing most of mankind.

What is a riddle? Many questions with clever or surprising answers, often involving a pun, are popularly called riddles but are, more exactly, conundrums. (Why does a cow go over a hill?—*Because she can't go under it.* Where can you hear a star sing?—*At the movies.*) Some conundrums are centuries old, some are freshly invented or adapted each year. A good many appear in our pages, to illustrate how this type of humorous riddling pastime passes from mouth to mouth, and from language to language.

The true riddle, however, always asks a question that can be answered reasonably. It generally does so by describing something in a way that at first suggests an answer other than the true one. (Little Nancy Etticoat, With a white petticoat And a red nose. She has no feet or hands, Yet the longer she stands, The shorter she grows.) In this favorite Mother Goose riddle, the name Nancy, the petticoat and the nose all suggest a girl. But her lack of hands and toes, and the fact that she grows *shorter*, at first confuse us and then lead to the solution *Candle*, which is completely logical. There are true riddles as absurd and funny as the most far-fetched conundrum. (What has one horn and gives milk?—*A milk truck.*) Here an animal is suggested, but the problem or paradox is that no animal, except the legendary unicorn, normally has but one horn. Some riddles contain shrewd folk comment and wit. (Treat me right, I'm everybody; Scratch my back, I'm nobody.—*A mirror.*) Some are as charming as nonsense rhymes for their verbal rigmarole. Many, like Nancy Etticoat and the beautiful riddle for *Water, sun, moon and stars* that begins our book, are poems in miniature.

Riddles are the world's oldest guessing games, and the popularity of these can be seen at almost any hour by flicking a radio or television dial. The posing and solution of riddles have interested man from the earliest antiquity to the present, and the art of riddling seems to be universal. In tiny Lithuania alone, over forty thousand folk riddles have been gathered. Among the major divisions of mankind, only the Chinese and the American Indians were long thought to lack riddles, but this no longer appears to be true.

In our grandfathers' day, riddles were a favorite game in our country for adults as well as children. At family and larger gatherings, old and young wits were tested with riddles and teased with catch questions. The clever ones were praised and sometimes rewarded, and those lacking skill might have to pay forfeits. In many countries these social and imaginative pastimes still delight people of all ages.

The riddle stories we have included will suggest the even greater importance of riddles long ago and in many countries. Many, like the amusing Mexican story, still circulate freely in the living folklore, though most of them refer to long past events. In these legends simple peasant boys win princesses and kingdoms by outriddling their superiors, kings gamble fortunes on their riddling skill, and even the god Odin leaves the sky to join the sport. Other themes are developed in other stories, showing still other uses or fabled uses of riddles in the past.

The Biblical tradition is full of such stories. The most famous is that of Samson in the Bible (Judges xiv), who gave his bride-to-be a riddle as their secret and killed thirty of her countrymen because she betrayed it. King Solomon is said to have won a fortune at riddling with another king, which he lost in a later bout. When the Queen of Sheba met Solomon, she tested his famed wisdom with over twenty riddles, all of which he answered. Today, in the Jewish Passover ritual, thirteen solemn questions are asked in riddle form. (Who knows one?—*I know one. One is our God in heaven and on the earth.* Who knows two?—*I know two. Two are the tables of the covenant....*)

The Hindu book of sacred hymns, the *Rig-Veda*, has many riddles to illustrate religious concepts. So has the *Koran* of Islam. And in the *Arabian Nights*, a young girl, paragon of beauty and intelligence, is tested lengthily in all branches of knowledge—religion, science, poetry and riddles (457th and 458th nights)—performing brilliantly in all. Halfway round the world in the Hawaiian Islands, we are told, chieftains used to compete at riddling as they did at boxing and wrestling and spear throwing, sometimes staking their lives on the outcome. One Hawaiian story tells of a lad whose slain father's bones lay bleaching before the house of a chieftain famous for riddling. By outdoing the chief and all his friends in a long riddling contest, the lad avenged his father's death.

Many other past and present uses of the riddle have been described. At ancient Greek banquets, the guests who could solve the most riddles were crowned with laurel, like victorious athletes. Fiji Island youngsters choose up sides for riddle-guessing, and the losers must give a feast for the winners. In certain Turkish tribes in Asia girls test the intellectual fitness of young men with riddles, rejecting the dull ones as suitors. In a Celebes tribe, riddles can be asked only when crops are growing. Then farmers sit in the fields and ask riddles. At the right answer, all chant, "Let our rice grow!" They believe that success in riddling will guarantee successful crops.

The most varied use of riddles today appears to be in Africa. Here they are used widely for entertainment by young and old as elsewhere, Kxatla children often forming sides for the game, much as in Fiji. Among the Makua and other tribes, riddles play a part in the important initiation rites by which boys and girls pass into adulthood. In some tribes men stake large bets on champion riddlers, and some groups are said to use riddles as ordeals, to establish innocence or guilt in juridical procedure. Sometimes also mental skill is exercised and tested by answering proverb with proverb, in an exchange resembling riddle and answer. No peoples in the world have riddles (or proverbs) more beautiful or more compacted with wisdom and humor than those found in Africa.

Nearly all the riddles in this book are folk riddles; that is, most were clearly gathered from the minds of people who had learned them orally from others. Nobody can guess who invented them or how they evolved. Yet there have been times when people consciously created riddles. Greek and Roman schoolboys, for example, were taught to sharpen their minds by constructing riddles, and among the latter it was a regular school subject. Serious poets have also composed riddles. Some of the most beautiful Anglo-Saxon poems were riddles, and among later writers who wrote riddles were Goethe, Voltaire and Cervantes. Writers have often reworked folk riddles into literary riddles, which sometimes then move into oral tradition, though it oftener happens nowadays that a folk riddle passes from lip to print and then back to lip again. The processes of folklore transmission can be very complicated in a world where many people know how to read. The majority of riddles printed here, however, undoubtedly came from people without books and the knowledge of reading.

Only through endless repetitions could we have shown how riddles—like folktales—run round the world. Yet for a number of riddles, notably those with the solutions *Teeth and mouth*, *Egg*, *Needle* and some combination of the natural elements *Sky, Sun, Moon and Stars*, we have given very wide representation. These well illustrate not only the world-wide diffusion of riddles, but the striking variety of metaphor and local imagery with which people everywhere have played on ancient familiar themes.

Often, of course, it is the solution which changes on these riddle migrations, rather than the question itself. In a beautiful Greek story, the little son of King Minos of Crete drowns in a honey vat, and his return to life is made possible because a wise man solves a riddle for *Mulberry*. (What is first white, then red, then black?) Every American child still knows the riddle, with elaborated details and the answer *Blackberry*, and to Brazilians the solution of the riddle (with some adaptations) is *Coffee bean*. The widespread chain riddle describing 'a house within a house within a house' shows up in the United States as *Watermelon, Cantaloupe* or *Walnut*, and the Cape Verde Islands as *Coconut*. In faraway Japan, the "houses" are "shops"—and the solution is *Chestnut*. The reader will notice many such changes.

Quite often a riddle printed here for one country might just as well have appeared under any one of twenty others. The Albanian "What runs and runs and never gets tired?—*A river*" is known (with the answer *River* or *Water* or *Wind*) in scores of countries; and the charming Cuban riddle for *A top* (To make me dance they put on my coat. . . .) appears in most Spanish language collections. Many factors governed our choice of where to place one of these universal or near-universal riddles. The student interested in tracing and comparing distributions should consult *English Riddles from Oral Tradition* by Archer Taylor. There he will learn how folklorists classify riddles for comparative study, and can examine thousands of riddles from all over the world.

For each group represented we have attempted minimally to present something already familiar in one form or another, something humorous, something beautiful in concept or metaphor, and something particularly appropriate to the scene and culture. Our sources varied greatly for fulfilling all these criteria. The choice was very often among many hundreds or even thousands of riddles; for Ceylon we give all the riddles that we found. Our sorrow is in having had to exclude so many interesting and beautiful riddles for lack of space or because we considered them too unfamiliar in content and therefore too difficult. These were from cultures most unlike our own. Yet we knew we could depend on the willingness of readers to yield up their imaginations to the lovely imagery of riddles from Asia, Africa and other distant regions, however strange and unfamiliar they may at first seem. In translating or adapting riddles from other languages, we have sometimes simplified them, or turned a non-interrogative riddle into a question, or added a query (such as "What is it?"). We have also substituted standard forms for a very few dialect words, especially in some Scottish riddles. However, we have tried to adhere strictly to the original intellectual content of all riddles. Much loss occurs, of course, in beauty and association, when a riddle is translated, especially when it is changed from rhyme to prose.

Our debt of gratitude to the many upon whose work we have drawn is expressed in the Acknowledgments and list of Sources at the back of this book.

NORTH AMERICA

Horn

A man was condemned to be hanged unless he could make up a riddle the king couldn't guess, so he made up this one:

Horn ate a horn up a high oak tree.
Guess this riddle and you can hang me.

The king couldn't guess and the man had to give him the answer: A man named Horn climbed a tree and ate a piece of candy shaped like a horn. With this riddle he saved his life.

—UNITED STATES

[13]

CANADA

I have a sheet, I can't fold it;
I have so much money I can't count it;
I have an apple and can't eat it;
I have a diamond and can't face it.
                    —*Water, stars, moon and sun.*

Two n's two o's an l and a d:
Now see what you can spell for me.—*London.*

In spring I am gay
In handsome array;
In summer more clothing I wear.
When colder it grows,
I fling off my clothes,
And in winter quite naked appear.—*A tree.*

What grows in the woods,
Winters in town,
And earns its master
Many a crown?—*A violin.*

Ten men's length,
Ten men's strength,
Ten men can't tear (it),
Yet a little boy walks off with it.—*A rope.*

[14]

Patch upon Patch,
Patch upon brown;
Two legs up,
Four legs down.—*A man named Patch, in a (patched) brown
suit, rode a horse named Patch.*

Full to the brim,
Without crack or seam.—*An egg.*

It wasn't the moon,
It wasn't the stars,
Yet it lighted the fields.—*Fireflies.*

[15]

Big as a barn,
Light as a feather,
And sixty horses can't pull it.—*The shadow of a barn.*

It wasn't my sister nor my brother,
But still was the child of my father and mother.
Who was it?—*Myself.*

What force or strength cannot get through,
I, with gentle touch, can do;
And many in the street could stand,
Were I not, as a friend, at hand.—*A key.*

What is that which, after we have bolted and locked the
door, placed a watchman on guard, and taken the keys with
us, yet, before morning, goes out in spite of us?

—*Fire in the grate.*

Four fingers and a thumb,
Yet flesh and blood have I none.—*A glove.*

Acts like a cat,
Looks like a cat,
Yet it isn't a cat.
What is it?—*A kitten.*

Why is a cherry like a book?—*Because it is red (read).*

Why is a hen like a penny?—*Both have a head and a tail.*

Why did the sparrow fly over the stone wall?
                              —*He couldn't fly through it.*

Where does all the snuff go?—*No one nose (knows).*

What is the first thing a man plants in his garden?
                              —*His foot.*

What makes more noise under a gate than a pig does?
                              —*Two pigs.*

What is the difference between your granny and your granary?
              —*One is your born kin; the other is your corn bin.*

What is the difference between a postage stamp and a mule?
—*One you stick with a lick and the other you lick with a stick.*

What is the difference between an automobile, a sigh and
a monkey?—*The first is so dear, the second is oh dear, and
the third is* you, *Dear.*

Newfoundland

In yonder valley there runs a deer,
With golden horns and silver hair;
It's neither fish, flesh, feather nor bone;
In yonder valley it runs alone.—*The sun.*

Round as a hoop,
Deep as a pail,
Never sings out
Till it's caught by the tail.—*A bell.*

What is it floats on the water as light as a feather,
And a thousand men couldn't lift it?—*A bubble.*

There's a tree in the valley,
Fifty-two branches round;
Each bears seven,
Which the Lord sent from Heaven.—*The year, weeks and days.*

As green as grass,
As black as coal;
Along came a silly soul
And popped it in his grinning hole.—*A blackberry.*

Ten drag
Woolly bag
Over calf hill.—*Putting on a woolen stocking.*

What is it that belongs to you,
But others use it more than you do?—*Your name.*

What goes over the water
And under the water
And never touches the water?—*An egg inside a duck.*

Long, slim and slender,
Tickles where it's tender.—*A horsewhip.*

Dene Indians of Arctic Canada

What animal drags his shovel along the trail?—*The beaver.*

What flies up ringing a bell?—*A mosquito.*

What comes down the mountain flashing like fire?
$$—A\ red\ fox's\ tail.$$

What is not to be touched?—*A briar bush.*

What glides through the air?—*An arrow.*

What looks like a heap of bones on the bottom of a shallow stream?—*Sticks gnawed by beavers.*

What looks like a herd of deer lying down?
$$—Bare\ spots\ of\ earth\ amid\ the\ snow,\ in\ spring.$$

I do not play, but I make others play. What am I?—*A ball.*

What sticks its head into the fire?—*A log.*

UNITED STATES
HAITI · PUERTO RICO
BRITISH WEST INDIES

UNITED STATES

On yonder hill there is a red deer,
The more you shoot, the more you may,
You cannot drive that deer away.—*The sun*.

What has eight legs, two arms, three heads, and wings?
        —*A man on horseback with a canary on his hand.*

Round as a biscuit,
Busy as a bee,
Prettiest little thing
You ever did see—*A watch*.

Over on the hill there is a little green house:
Inside the green house there's a little white house;
Inside the white house there's a little red house;
Inside the red house there are a lot of little babies.
                        —*A watermelon*.

Round and round and round the shack,
Peeking in at every crack.—*The wind*.

What's long and slim and works in the light,
Has but one eye and an awful bite?—*A needle*.

Little Jessie Ruddle,
Settin' in a puddle,
Green garters and yaller toes.
Tell me that riddle
Or I'll mash your nose.—*A duck*.

Long, slim and slender,
Dark as homemade thunder,
Keen eyes and peaked nose,
Scares the devil wherever he goes.—*A snake*.

Round as an apple,
Rough as a bear,
If you guess this riddle,
You may pull my hair.—*A walnut*.

White as snow, but snow it ain't;
Green as grass, but grass it ain't;
Red as blood, but blood it ain't;
Black as coal, but coal it ain't.—*A blackberry*.

What loves a dog and rides on his back,
He can travel for miles and not leave a track?—*A flea*.

As I was going across London Bridge,
I peeped down through a crack.
I saw Old Mother Hubbard
With a blanket on her back.—*A mud turtle*.

A teakettle is a teakettle,
A teakettle has what everything has.
Now what has a teakettle?—*A name*.

What won't go up the chimney up,
But will go up the chimney down?
What won't go down the chimney up,
But will go down the chimney down?—*An umbrella.*

Round as an apple and thin as a knife;
Answer this riddle and I'll be your wife.—*A dime.*

Yonder in the field stands a big red bull;
He eats and eats, but he never gets full.—*A threshing machine.*

My face is marked,
My hands a-movin';
Got no time to play,
Got to run all day.—*A clock.*

Little red thing on the hill:
Give it hay, it will live;
Give it water, it will die.—*A fire.*

A little fence that's always wet,
But never has been rained on yet.—*The teeth.*

Treat me right,
I look like everybody;
Scratch my back,
I look like nobody.—*A mirror.*

Never sings a melody, never has a song,
But it goes humming all day long.—*A sawmill.*

Strange Names

Over on the hill there is a pony,
All saddled, All bridled, All ready to go.
I've told you his name three times,
And still you don't know.—*The pony's name is All.*

As I went down the lane,
I rode, and Yet I walked.—*Yet I is a dog.*

There was a hill, you know,
And on the hill, you know,
There was a house, you know,
And in the house, you know,
There was a table, you know,
And under the table, you know,
There was a dog, you know.
What was his name, you know?—*Uno was the dog's name.*

What goes all over the floor in the daytime and stands in the corner at night?—*The broom.*

What goes all over the pasture in the daytime and sits in the cupboard at night?—*Milk.*

What goes all over the pasture, goes to the creek, goes into the water over its head, and doesn't drink?—*A horseshoe nail.*

What goes with the wagon, stops when the wagon stops, is no good to the wagon, yet the wagon can't go without it?
                                        —*The squeak.*

If two men went hunting, and shot a jaybird, which they cooked and ate, what would their telephone number be?
                                        —*281 J. (Two ate one jay.)*

Where do the fish wash their faces?—*In the river basin.*

A nickel and a dime were sitting on a fence and the nickel fell off. Why didn't the dime fall? —*It had more sense (cents).*

If you see twenty dogs running down the street, what time is it?—*Nineteen after one.*

What do folks call little gray cats back in Tennessee?—*Kittens.*

What is big at the bottom, little at the top, and has ears?
                                        —*A mountain. (It has mountaineers.)*

Comanche Indians

What looks like a star in the water?—*A fish's eye.*

What is it that grows big where it sits down?—*A wood tick.*

What is it that for one day has his own way?—*A prairie fire.*

Who is that good-looking young person in the white-striped blanket?—*A skunk.*

Who is the girl who always wears yellow paint on her cheeks?
—*A raccoon.*

What animal is stronger than all the others?—*The skunk.*

What is it, running along, with no sense?—*An automobile.*

Arapaho Indians

What has many branches and is yet very light?
                    —An eagle breath feather.

What are the two that never get tired of motion?*—The eyelids.*

What are the most sacred things?*—Day, night and the earth.*

Which of the two is the greatest benefactor, man or wife?
            —They are equally good in every particular.

MEXICO

Tito, Tito, with his paper cape,
Climbs to the sky and lets out a yell.
                    —A rocket shot off at a fiesta.

A little mud hut is filled with little dark people,
And a little wooden caretaker tends it.
          —An earthen pot full of beans, and a wooden spoon.

Drums beat in the high towers,
And ladies dance in the lower rooms.
                    —Thunder, and rain splashing in pools.

What is it, what is it: it overcomes you and you never see it?
                                        —Sleep.

When you plant corn, what is the first thing that appears?
                              —A pig to root it up.

Why must the *padre* (priest) go to the altar to say mass?
            —Because the altar won't come to him.

What is the resemblance between a piano and a hairbrush?
                    —Neither can climb a tree.

16th-Century Aztec Riddles

What is it, what is it: it travels up a valley clapping and clapping like a woman making bread?—*A butterfly flying.*

What is it, what is it: you get into it by three roads and get out of it by one?—*A shirt.*

What is it, what is it: a mirror with a house made of pine boughs?—*The eye and eyelashes.*

What is it, what is it: it is completely gray-haired and grows green plumes?—*An onion.*

What is it, what is it: a blue jar sown with toasted corn?
—The sky and stars.

Yucatan

Four stampers,
Two lookers,
Two man-killers
And a fly-killer.—*A bull.*

Over a flat rock is inverted a white gourd. What is it?
—The moon.

Over a flat rock is inverted the redness of a tomato. What is it?—*The sun.*

The Riddle of Foolish Juan

There was once a country boy whom everybody called Foolish Juan. One day the king announced that whoever asked the princess a riddle she couldn't answer could marry her, but whoever asked her a riddle she *could* answer would pay with his life. Lots of people came, hoping to ask her riddles she couldn't answer, but she answered everybody and the king had them all shot.

"Well," Foolish Juan said to his mother, "I'm going to the king's palace to ask his daughter a riddle she can't answer." The mother told him not to, but he went anyway. When he got there and found the princess, he asked,

> Foundation over foundation,
> Over the foundation a box,
> Over the box a cross,
> Over the cross a mill,
> Over the mill two caves,
> Over the two caves two lights,
> Over the two lights a hill,
> Over the hill trees,
> And upon the trees robbers.
> Tell me what that is!

The princess thought and thought and couldn't guess, so Foolish Juan said, "The first foundation is the feet, the second foundation is the legs, the box is the body, the cross is the arms, the mill is the mouth, the two caves are the nostrils, the two lights are the eyes, the hill is the head, the trees are the hair and the robbers are lice. So let's get married!"

And the princess married Foolish Juan.

—*A Mexican folktale, slightly adapted.*

[30]

CUBA

There is a convent shut up tight,
Without any bells or towers;
And in it many little nuns
Are making sweets from flowers.—*A beehive and bees.*

Going down the road I saw a little boy with a yellow shirt on,
and I took off his shirt and ate him.—*A banana.*

What is green on the mountain, black in the market place,
and red in the house?—*Charcoal.*

A little black bull fell into the sea:
No one could catch it and no rope could hold it.—*Night.*

Locked in a narrow prison, and guarded by ivory soldiers,
There is a red snake who is the mother of lies.—*The tongue.*

To make me dance, they put on my coat,
Because I can't dance without it;
To make me dance, they take off my coat,
Because I can't dance with it on.—*A top and string.*

In an orchard I saw a dog who bit me forty times before I
could take away one of her pups. What is that?
                    —*A lemon tree, its thorns and a lemon.*

[31]

Why does a watch always stop when it falls on the floor?
                    —*Because it can't go through the floor.*

How can you eat an egg without breaking the shell?
                              —*Have someone else break it.*

I went up the mountain,
And there I saw a tree:
The tree had a nest;
The nest had an egg;
The egg had a hair;
When I pulled the hair, the nest screamed.—*A bell in a steeple.*

If an elephant fell into a thirty-foot well, how would you
get it out?—*Wet.*

What animal eats with its tail?
                    —*All do, because no animal removes his tail to eat.*

HAITI

Ra-ta-ta roared and the roar was heard in Africa. What is that?—*Thunder.*

A big cathedral is broken and no workmen can repair it. What is it?—*An egg.*

My mother has a little boy: whatever you want him to do, you have to hold him by the neck. What is it?—*A jar.*

My mother has a little girl: whatever you want her to do, you have to hold her by the hip. What is it?—*A cup.*

My father has a tree: all the leaves are words. What is it?
—*A book.*

My father has a fish that swims in only one pool. What is it?—*The tongue.*

I have a house: I've painted it green outside, its living room white and its bedroom pink; many black soldiers are shut up inside.—*A watermelon.*

PUERTO RICO

I came from Santo Domingo,
Talking like a priest;
I have a little green body,
And a red heart in my breast. —*A parrot.*

Dangly-dangly is hanging:
Grunty-grunty is watching.
If Dangly-dangly should fall,
Grunty-grunty would eat it up.
>   —*A pig eying nuts on a palm tree.*

Why is a candle flame like thirst?
>   —*A little water will end both.*

Why is a writing pen like an umbrella?
>   —*Both must be wet to be useful.*

A blind man, an armless man and a naked man were walking
down a path. The blind man saw a fish, the armless man
picked it up and the naked man put it in his pocket. What
is that?—*A lie!*

BRITISH WEST INDIES

Barbados

There's a cow—when it groans you can hear it all over the world.—*Thunder.*

I have a little sister; the more you feed her the more she cries.—*A frying pan.*

Jamaica

My father has a rose tree in his yard. Every night the roses bloom, but in the morning every rose is gone.—*The stars.*

John Redman tickled John Blackman until he laughed. What is that?—*The fire made the pot boil.*

My father has a man: he can't stand up until his belly is full.—*A sack.*

My father has a horse: you hold him by the ears and he bites with his tail.—*Scissors.*

Miss Nancy was going to Kingston and dropped her handkerchief, but she didn't stop to pick it up. What is that?
—*A bird dropped a feather.*

[35]

Grenada

My mother has a boy: he always wears a black suit which he never changes. What is he?—*A blackbird.*

My mother has a girl: every step she takes she opens her white handkerchief. What is she?—*A sea wave and foam.*

My mother sent a boy for the doctor, and the doctor came before the boy could get back. What is that?
> —*A boy climbed a tree for a coconut, which reached the ground before he could climb down.*

Bahamas

My father had a bunch of bananas, and nobody could pick one.—*A wasp nest.*

My father had a big rooster, and every time he crowed he crowed fire.—*A gun.*

My father had ten sons and every one wore his cap on the back of his head.—*Fingers and nails.*

My father has a horse, and every time he jumps he leaves a piece of his tail behind.—*A needle and thread.*

SOUTH AMERICA

The Observant Man

Two men met on a road and the first one asked, "Did you see a lost horse on this road?"

The second man replied, "Was he lame in the left front leg, blind in the right eye, lacking some front teeth and dragging a long rope?"

"Yes," said the first man, "that is my horse. Where did he go?"

"I didn't see him," replied the second.

"Then how do you know so much about him?"

"I can tell by the tracks in the road that a horse passed by, protecting his lame left front leg as he walked. I can see that he grazed only on the left side of the road and so must have been blind in his right eye. I can tell from the unbitten blades of grass that some front teeth were missing from his mouth. And anybody can see the track left here in the road by the dragging rope."

—A CUBAN FOLKTALE

BRAZIL

Green as grass,
Red as blood,
Sweet as honey,
Bitter as gall.—*A coffee bean.*

On high I live, on high I dwell:
Everyone sees me, no one worships me.—*Bell in the steeple.*

On high I live, on high I dwell:
No one sees me, everyone worships me.—*God.*

Many maidens dressed in yellow live in a green castle.
Who are they?—*Oranges on a tree.*

What is it, what is it: a tall man with his arms spread
out and a flower on his chest?—*A lamp post.*

What is it, what is it: a row of girls dressed in yellow lean
out the grocer's window?—*Bananas.*

Tico-tico, pinirico,
Has no feet, has no beak-O,
But later he will grow them.—*A woodpecker egg.*

What is it, what is it: the clothing a woman wears, which
her husband never sees?—*Mourning.*

What is it, what is it: a tiny man all covered with pock marks?—*A thimble.*

What was born standing up and runs lying down?—*A log canoe.*

What is it, what is it: a crazy one inside a big corral?
—*The tongue and mouth.*

Tell me, lady, lady,
Since you are so wise,
What's the bird that flies,
And gives milk to its baby?—*A bat.*

ARGENTINA

What speaks without thinking, cries without sadness, laughs without humor, and tells lies without knowing it?—*A parrot.*

Everybody asks for me;
I don't ask for anybody.
Everybody tramples on me;
I don't trample on anybody.—*A street.*

What is round and transparent, and with all the colors of the rainbow? A single breath of air created it and another will end it.—*A soap bubble.*

Under Pearily-Pearily
Lay Sleepy-Sleepy,
And Wiggly-Wiggly came
To bite Sleepy-Sleepy.
But Pearily-Pearily fell
And woke up Sleepy-Sleepy,
Who killed Wiggly-Wiggly
And ate Pearily-Pearily.
—A man was sleeping under a pear tree, when a snake came. A pear fell, waking him. He killed the snake and ate the pear.

You see me in the street and you leave me in the street. I enter every house, only to get thrown out of each one.
—Dust.

What is the talkative parrot shut up in a bone corral?
—*The tongue.*

Who is the girl dressed in green who has a red heart?
—*A watermelon.*

What can carry a hundred bushels of potatoes but can't lift a quail?—*A river.*

What did Columbus see on his right hand when he discovered America?—*Five fingers.*

What ripples like water but isn't a river,
Has a beard like a goat but isn't a goat?—*Wheat in the field.*

How does a front door resemble a drunk man?
—*Both get locked up.*

Can anyone jump higher than a thirty-foot wall?
—*Yes. A wall can't jump.*

CHILE

What is the little mule that carries a load into a ditch and comes out without it?—*A spoon, carrying food into the mouth.*

I shall die in a jail that I built myself,
And rich garments will be made from its walls.
Who am I?—*A silkworm.*

What is the field where you cut down the shrubbery but don't pull it out?—*The head and the hair.*

What is the little lamb that stands on one foot in the pasture and eats nothing?—*A mushroom.*

Who am I: When impudent people hit my shining white teeth with their fists, I cry out loudly?—*A piano.*

I'm so devout that I call everybody to mass;
Yet I never hear the mass, though I live in the church.
                                                    —The church bell.

I have muscles of steel, and I spend the year talking with half the people in the world. Who am I?—*The telegraph line.*

I am round as the moon: people crush me, skin me, drink my blood and throw my skin away.—*A grape.*

A lot of little brothers live in one house, and if you only scratch their heads they will die. What are they?

—*Matches in a box.*

What is the bowlful of hazelnuts that is scattered out at night and gathered up in the morning?—*The stars.*

What is the bowlful of hazelnuts that is gathered up at night and scattered out in the morning?—*Cattle (corraled at night, and sent to the pasture in the morning).*

PERU & PARAGUAY

PARAGUAY

What is the tile-roofed house that moves on four corner posts?—*An armadillo.*

Big listeners,
Slim ground-touchers,
And a little fly-frightener—
What's that?—*A donkey.*

Some pretty girls come into the house but soon rush out with their faces red. What is that?—*Firewood and sparks.*

What musician invites death every time he sings to you?
—*A mosquito.*

A bull lies under the ground but his rope runs on the ground.
—*A sweet potato and its vine.*

What is raised in the forest and ends its life on the altar?
—*Beeswax. (Candles are made from it.)*

Something roars, but it isn't a bull;
It runs, but it isn't a river.—*It is a sugar mill.*

[45]

PERU

Who goes around barefoot, yet wears golden spurs and a red necktie?—*A rooster.*

On a blue plain there is a piece of bread that someone has tossed away. What is that?—*The moon.*

When the big black one starts going crazy, the little black one calms her down. What is that?—*A big pot and a spoon.* (*When the pot boils too high it is stirred.*)

There is a man who is very tiny but very angry. Who is he?
—*Red pepper.*

What is the red flag that keeps waving inside a cave?
—*The tongue and mouth.*

Mama beats a drum, papa blows a horn and the children start chattering. What is that?—*A hen pecking the earth, a rooster crowing, and the little chicks cheeping.*

I went to the market in the plaza:
There I bought a pretty little girl;
I brought her home and wept over her.—*An onion.*

[46]

BRITISH ISLES

Merry Riddles of Long Ago*

What is it that goeth about the wood and cannot
get in?—*It is the bark of a tree.*

What is it that goeth through the wood and
leaveth on every bush a rag?—*It is the snow.*

What is it that goeth through the wood and
toucheth never a twig?—*It is the blast of a horn.*

What is it that I can hold in my hand, and it will
not lie in a great chest?—*It is a long spear.*

What is it that is higher than a house,
And yet seems much lesser than a mouse?
                                   —A star in the sky.

Down in a dale there sits and stands,
Eight legs and two hands,
Livers and lights and lives three.
I count him wise that tells this to me.
*—A man on horseback with a hunting hawk in his
hand.*

* From *The Booke of Merry Riddles*, London, 1629.

[47]

ENGLAND SCOTLAND IRELAND WALES

ENGLAND

Long waist, brazen face,
No great thing of beauty;
It stands most bright by day or night,
Performing of its duty.—*A grandfather clock.*

I have a cock on yonder hill,
I keep him for a wonder,
And every time that cock doth crow,
It lightens, hails and thunders.—*A gun.*

As red as an apple,
As round as a ball,
Higher than the steeple,
Weathercock and all.—*The sun.*

As I was going along a road, I met a little man with a
blue coat and yellow breeches on. He said, "Um, ha! I
care for no man!" Who was he?—*A wasp.*

Clink, clank, doon the bank,
Ten against four;
Splish, splash, in the dish,
Till it run o'er.—*Milking a cow.*

Jackatawad ran over the moor,
Never behind but always before.—*Will o' the wisp.*

Behind the bush, behind the thorn,
I heard a stout man blow his horn.
He was booted and spurred and stood with pride,
With golden feathers at his side.
His beard was flesh and his mouth was horn.
I am sure such a man never could have been born.
                                        —*A rooster.*

Yonder stands a tree of honor,
Twelve limbs grow upon her,
Every limb a different name.
It would take a wise man to tell you the same.—*The year with its months.*

Arthur O'Bower has broken his band;
He comes roaring up the land.
The King of Scots, for all his power,
Cannot turn Arthur of the Bower.—*A windstorm.*

Hibbledy hobbledy greasy,
When he's out he's all about,
When he's in he's easy.—*A fish out of water.*

It's in the rock, but not in the stone;
It's in the marrow, but not in the bone;
It's in the bolster, but not in the bed;
It's not in the living, nor yet in the dead.—*The letter R.*

London Bridge

As I was going over London Bridge,
I saw a steel house;
It had four and twenty windows,
And wouldn't hold a mouse.—A *thimble*.

As I was going o'er London Bridge,
I heard something crack;
Not a man in England
Can mend that!—*Ice*.

As I was going over London Bridge,
I met a load of soldiers,
Some in ickets, some in ackets,
Some in red and yellow jackets.
What were they?—A *swarm of wasps*.

As I was going over London Bridge,
I met a load of hay.
I shot with my pistol,
And all flew away.—A *flock of birds*.

As I was going over London Bridge,
I peeped into a winder,
And I saw four and twenty ladies,
Dancing on a cinder.—*Sparks*.

As I went over Lincoln Bridge,
I met Mister Rusticap,
Pins and needles on his back,
A-going to Thorny Fair.—A *hedgehog*.

Round the House

Round the house and round the house,
And leaves a white glove in the window.—*Snow*.

Round the house and round the house,
And leaves a black glove in the window.—*Rain*.

Round the house and round the house,
And in my lady's chamber.—*Sunshine*.

Mother Goose Riddles*

Humpty Dumpty sat on a wall,
Humpty Dumpty had a great fall.
  All the king's horses
  And all the king's men
Couldn't put Humpty together again.—*An egg*.

As I was going to St. Ives,
I met a man with seven wives,
Each wife had seven sacks,
Each sack had seven cats,
Each cat had seven kits.
Kits, cats, sacks and wives,
How many were going to St. Ives?—*One*.

There was a girl in our town,
Silk an' satin was her gown,
Silk an' satin, gold an' velvet,
Guess her name, three times I've telled it.—*Ann*.

* These are among the "classic" English nursery rhyme riddles known in every
English-speaking country.

Little Nancy Etticoat,
With a white petticoat,
And a red nose.
She has no feet or hands,
Yet the longer she stands,
The shorter she grows.—*A lighted candle.*

Old Mother Twitchett has but one eye,
And a long tail which she lets fly,
And every time she goes over a gap,
She leaves a bit of her tail in a trap.—*A needle and thread.*

I have a little sister, they call her Peep-Peep,
She wades the waters, deep, deep, deep;
She climbs the mountains, high, high, high;
Poor little creature, she has but one eye.—*A star.*

Thirty white horses
Upon a red hill;
Now they tramp,
Now they champ,
Now they stand still.—*The teeth and tongue.*

As round as an apple,
As deep as a cup,
All the king's horses
Can't pull it up.—*A well.*

As soft as silk,
As white as milk,
As bitter as gall;
A thick wall,
And a green coat covers me all.—*A walnut.*

[53]

SCOTLAND

Aberdeen and Aberdour;
Spell that in letters four.—*T H A T*.

White bird featherless
Flew from Paradise,
Perched upon the castle wall.
Up came Lord John Landless,
Took it up handless,
And road away horseless
To the King's white hall.—*Snow (melted by the sun)*.

It's as round's the moon,
An' as clear's crystal;
An ye dinna tell me ma riddle,
I'll shoot ye wi' ma pistol!—*A watch*.

As round's the moon, as yellow's ochre;
If ye dinna tell me that, I'll feel ye wi' the poker.—*An orange*.

White mare on the hill,
With her foal at her heel.—*The moon and a star nearby*.

The robbers came to our hoose
When we were a' in;
The hoose leapt out at the windows,
And we were a' ta'en.—*Fishes caught in a net*.

[54]

Doon in the wood I aince did grow,
Till the saw did me destroy;
Syne (since then) by the axe I was made alive,
An' noo I sing wi' joy.—*A fiddle.*

Throo the woods and throo the woods,
And throo the woods I ran;
And every bus' (bush) that I cam till,
I left my rags and ran.—*A sheep left its wool on every thorn.*

As I went to Westminster School,
I saw a Westminster scholar.
He pulled off his hat *an' drew* off his gloves,
And I've told you the name of the scholar.—*Andrew.*

An' it neither Peg, Meg nor Margit
Is my true love's name;
An' it neither Peg, Meg nor Margit,
An' thrice I've told her name.—*Ann.*

Hobbity-Bobbity sits on this side o' the burn,
Hobbity-Bobbity sits on that side o' the burn;
An' gin ye touch Hobbity-Bobbity,
Hobbity-Bobbity'll bite ye!—*A nettle bush.*

What is it that goes out black and comes in white?
                    —*A black cow on a snowy day.*

What goes out between two woods and comes in between
two waters?—*A woman going for water with two wooden pails.*

How many toads' tails would it take to reach the moon?
                    —*One if it were long enough.*

WALES

What small chest is full of mouse bones?—*A cat.*

What tiny box is this: one can open it but a hundred can't shut it again?—*A nut.*

Where can you put a candle so that everybody in the room except you can see it?—*On your head.*

What fish has its ears farthest apart?—*The biggest fish.*

What is quicker than a fish?—*The one who can catch it.*

What is the blackest thing in the world, yet it spreads knowledge all over the world?—*Ink.*

What grows bigger if you leave it alone and smaller if you add something to it?—*A hole in a stocking.*

What is as old as the mountains?—*The valleys between them.*

What is a white, white lady
With a fire on her head?—*A candle.*

A slender grayhound runs over the hedge. It kills but never barks. What is it?—*A scythe.*

Welsh Gypsies

What goes to the city with its face turned backward and its back turned forward?—*A watch in your pocket.*

What grows head down and feet up?—*An onion.*

As big as a man, as empty as a box;
Lift up his tail and his nose will run.—*A pump.*

My grandmother used to boil pudding in her stocking. Explain that!—*She wore stockings when boiling the pudding.*

IRELAND

There was a man and no man,
He had a gun and no gun,
He shot a bird and no bird,
Upon a tree and no tree.
   —A boy with a popgun shot a butterfly on a hollyhock.

I washed my hands in water that never rained nor run;
I dried them in a towel was never wove nor spun.
                                        —Dew and sun.

In the garden's a castle with hundreds within,
Yet stripped to my shirt I would never fit in.—*An ant hill.*

Riddle me, riddle me, Randy Row,
My father gave me some seed to sow;
The seeds were black, the ground was white:
Riddle me that against Saturday night.
                          —Writing on white paper.

A white barrel with its end to you; everyone in Erin sees it.
What is it?—*The moon.*

Does be in the meadow but is never mown;
Does be in the river but is never drowned;
Does be in the shop but is never sold.—*The sun.*

Hicky-picky locked the gate,
Hicky-picky locked it weel,
Hicky-picky locked the gate,
Without iron or steel.—*Frost.*

As I was at my window,
I looked through my golden ring;
I saw the dead carrying the living.
Wasn't that a wondrous thing?—*A trainful of people.*

What goes away above the ground and returns under it?
              —*A man carrying sods on his head.*

I sat on my hunkers,
I looked through my peepers;
I saw the dead burying the living.
              —*Dead ashes falling on the fire.*

It comes in on men's shoulders,
And goes out on a silken thread.—*Smoke.*

A bottomless barrel,
It's shaped like a hive;
It is filled full of flesh,
And the flesh is alive.—*A tailor's thimble.*

What goes round the house and around the house and a
harrow after it?—*A hen, followed by her chickens.*

A milk-white gull through the air floats down,
And never a tree but he lights thereon.—*Snow.*

I threw it up as white as snow;
Like gold on a flag it fell below.—An egg.

A steel pig going over a bone bridge, and a brass man
driving it. What is that?—*A needle and a finger with thimble.*

A long white barn: two roofs on it and no door at all. What
is it?—*An egg.*

I went to the wood for a load of timber. I brought neither
long sticks nor short sticks, but I brought a load of timber.
What did I bring?—*Sawdust.*

What is full and yet will hold more?
      —*A pot full of potatoes before you pour water into it.*

As I went out one moonlight night,
I saw a thing that made me fright.
I hit it hard and heavy blows
Till it bled gallons at the nose.—*A pump.*

Little Jinny Whiteskin, she has a red nose,
And the longer she stands the shorter she grows.—*A candle.*

Spell Blackwater in three letters.—*I N K.*
Spell red rogue in three letters.—*F O X.*
Spell blackbird in four letters.—*C R O W.*

Is life worth living?—*That depends upon the liver.*

EUROPE & ASIA MINOR

The Clever Peasant Lad

One day the wealthy lord of a manor, who prided himself on being clever, stopped at a farmhouse door and found one of his peasant lads resting by the fire.

"Are you alone here?" he asked.

"No longer," the lad replied, "because I now see the half of two four-limbed ones."

"What are you doing?" the lord asked, puzzled.

"I am cooking what goes up and comes down."

"What is your father doing?"

"He is in the vineyard, doing good and harm."

"And your mother?"

"Before dawn she baked the bread we ate last week. Then early this morning she cut off the heads of the healthy to make the sick healthy. Just now she is driving away the hungry ones to feed those who aren't hungry."

The lord understood nothing of this and went angrily to the vineyard to tell the father all the boy had said.

"All that is very simple," the father explained. "What my son saw when you rode up to the door were your legs and the forelegs of your horse. What he is cooking is beans, that jump up and down in the boiling pot. Here in the vineyard I am pruning vines, and I am thus doing good by doing harm to the vines. As for my wife, before dawn she baked bread to repay a neighbor who lent us bread last week. Next she killed some chicken to make broth to feed her sick brother. And now she is keeping off the hens so that the geese will stuff themselves and grow very fat."

The wealthy lord was very angry at being outwitted by a peasant lad.

—PART OF A FRENCH FOLKTALE

[61]

FRANCE

Who is that rosy girl seated in a green armchair?
                                        —*A strawberry.*

What can outrun a horse and cross the water without getting wet?—*The sun.*

What is the plant that even blind people can recognize?
                                        —*A thorn bush.*

My father has a blanket he can't fold, my mother has a ball she can't roll, and my sister has so many coins she can't count them.—*The sky, the moon and the stars.*

How can a man make the moon dance?
        —*By tossing a stone at the moon reflected in water.*

A little old man stands in the middle of the field, and when it rains the rain falls only on his hat. What is it?—*A mushroom.*

The more you pull it by the tail, the further away from you it goes. What is it?—*A ball of string.*

What is the roundest thing in the sea?—*A fish's eye.*

What barnyard creature could write if she knew how to use what she has?—*A goose, if she knew how to use a quill.*

A little keg without a hoop: what is it?—*An egg.*

I have something but I don't have something else that I'd like
to have in order not to have what I have. What are they?
                                        —*Hunger and food.*

ITALY

A dancer dances in the center of a theater full of white chairs.—*The tongue and teeth.*

What can you see in winter that you can never see in summer?—*Your breath.*

Who is the young girl less than one month old who travels over the whole country?—*The moon.*

When I give it something to eat it cries, but when I give it nothing it is quiet. What is it?—A *frying pan.*

The more you take from it in front, the more you add to it behind. What is it?—*The road you are traveling on.*

In a little house without a door, the tenant knocks and knocks. He doesn't want to stay inside any longer, and if nobody opens up for him he'll break the door down. What is that?
—*A chick in an egg.*

He has a red hat but is not a cardinal;
He wears spurs but is not a knight.—*A rooster.*

What animal flies yet has no wings?—*The frog.*

I have a basket full of diamonds: Every evening they are scattered about and every morning they are gathered up again.—*The sky and the stars.*

I have something very cheap, yet it is good enough to clothe the king. What is it?—*A needle.*

I have five brothers and only one wears a hat. What is it?—*The fingers; one has a thimble on it.*

RUMANIA

I have a little bear, tied round and round with thousands of cords. What is it?—*A ball of string.*

What can pass through customs at the frontier without even being seen?—*The wind.*

What can cross a river without stirring up waves?—*A shout.*

What is it that women don't have and don't want? Men consider it a fine thing to have, but once they have it they try to get rid of it.—*A beard.*

Who spends the day at the window, goes to the table for meals and hides at night?—*A housefly.*

What can you throw into the air that won't fall back down?
—*A live bird.*

Who can go about town at night that the dogs won't bark at?—*Smoke.*

What is it that goes around all day grunting without being sick, and is always looking for something without having lost anything?—*A pig.*

SPAIN

What do ladies nearly always hold in their hands—sometimes
folded up and sometimes stretched out flat?—*A fan.*

[67]

Who is the little prisoner who always sings happy songs?
                              —*A bird in a cage.*

What runs and runs and never reaches its owner's house?
                                        —*A windmill.*

A thousand travel along one path, yet they kick up no dust.
What is that?—*Ants.*

What weaver sits spinning at her loom in the sky?—*A spider.*

I live on high, wearing a little golden crown;
Even if the Moors come, I cannot run away.
                              —*An acorn on a tree.*

What is this: the bigger it gets, the less you see it?—*Darkness.*

What may I have that God does not have?
                              —*A brother or a sister.*

What is as long as a road and as dirty as a pig?—*A river.*

What is the size of a cucumber and has whiskers like a
Capuchin monk?—*An ear of corn.*

We have two legs, but we can't go anywhere without a man—
and *he* can't go anywhere without us! What is that?—*Trousers.*

PORTUGAL

There are three things:
One says, "Let's go!"
One says, "Let's stay!"
One says, "Let's dance!"—*Water, sand and foam.*

I sowed little flat boards and harvested barrels. Riddle me
that, scholars!—*Pumpkin seeds and pumpkins.*

What is the thing that was alive
And now is dead—
But carries five little live ones
Inside its head?—*A leather shoe with five toes inside it.*

Two hundred armed soldiers are lined up on a battlefield.
What is that?—*A paper of pins.*

Pine under linen,
Flowers over linen,
And roundabout sit loved ones.
What is that?
—*A table, the cloth, flowers on the table and a family dining.*

My father and mother were great singers, though neither one
had any teeth. As for myself, I am very white and completely
bald, and I have a yellow heart. What am I?—*An egg.*

What are these: As soon as they enter their house they stick
their heads out the windows?—*Buttons and buttonholes.*

Cape Verde Islands

There is a little green grass house:
Inside the little green grass house
There is a little tiled house;
Inside the little tiled house
There is a little white house;
Inside the little white house
There is a tank of water.—*A coconut.*

What is poor at the bottom and poor at the top, but rich
in the middle?—*A cornstalk with corn on it.*

I have a daughter: she goes away by land and comes back
by water.—*A turtle.*

Ten men live in the same house and each has his own room:
If one makes a mistake all the others make a mistake.
                    —*The buttons and buttonholes on a garment.*

Two walk into the country: the one with two feet gets tired,
but the one with one foot doesn't tire.
                    —*A man went walking with a cane.*

Little chases Big out of the room: what is that?
                    —*A lamp and darkness.*

There is a man with two eyes: one sees by day and the
other sees by night. What are they?—*The sun and the moon.*

BELGIUM

How can one step into the wood without seeing a single tree?—*By putting on wooden shoes.*

What dances around the yard after it is dead?—*A fallen leaf.*

What is no bigger than a colt's hoof and yet can raise up a whole bushel of wheat?—*A cake of yeast.*

A beautiful king dressed in red lives in a palace made of flesh and bones, guarded by two rows of soldiers. What is that?—*The tongue, mouth and teeth.*

What is no bigger than an almond and yet fills the whole room?—*A candle flame.*

What sings as it goes into the earth and weeps as it climbs out?—*A well bucket.*

What goes round the house dragging a mop behind it?
—*A cat with its tail.*

Guess this, you! What goes up into the air round and comes down with a tail?—*A ball of string.*

Guess this, you! What often threatens you, but can't say a word to you?—*A forefinger.*

HOLLAND

Amsterdam, the beautiful city, built on piles driven into the mud! Tell me how many letters are in *that?—Four*.

He who has it doesn't tell it;
He who takes it doesn't know it;
He who knows it doesn't want it.
What is it?—*Counterfeit money*.

Black said to Red,
"Break me and you're dead!"—*Pot and fire*.

What can you cover with a tub, yet can't drag away with a thousand horses?—*A well*.

First they pounded me,
Then they beat me to pieces,
Then they took my skin off,
Then they ate me.—*A nut*.

GERMANY

There are four brothers in the world:
The first runs but never gets tired;
The second eats but is never satisfied;
The third drinks but is never full;
The fourth sings but his song is not pleasant to the ear.
—*Water, fire, the earth and the wind.*

What am I: if you want to have more of me you must bury
me?—*Grain seeds.*

What picture hangs on the wall without a nail?—*A shadow.*

In spring I delight you,
In summer I cool you,
In autumn I feed you,
In winter I warm you.—*A tree (bloom, shade, fruit, fuel).*

What is nakeder than naked—
So naked that it knocks?—*A skeleton.*

Who goes yonder through the grass? He has a long nose, wears
red stockings and struts like a nobleman?—*A stork.*

What is not very long and not very short and always just
a foot long?—*A shoe.*

Who is it that can boast of the greatest deeds in the world?
>*—A braggart.*

I have more money in my pocket than the richest merchant in Hamburg. Do you believe that?
>*—Yes. He has no money in your pocket.*

What kind of stones do you generally see in the Rhine?
>*—Wet ones.*

Where do the fox and the hare lie down peacefully together?
>*—In the fur shop.*

Guess, what is the most faithful animal?
>*—The louse. Once it finds a friend it clings to him.*

The Enchanted Woman

Three women were enchanted into flowers growing in a field, but one of them was allowed to return home each night as a woman. Early one morning, before she had to go back as a flower to her companions in the field, she said to her husband, "If you will come this afternoon and pluck me, I shall be set free and can henceforth stay here with you."

He did so, but how did he know which flower to pluck, since all three looked exactly alike?

ANSWER: Since she had passed the night at home and not in the field, no dew fell on her, as it did on the others. By this her husband knew her.

SWITZERLAND

What shouts along the street,
And hasn't any lung?
He licks up snow like sugar,
Yet hasn't any tongue.—*The wind.*

What's as small as a mouse,
Yet it fills a whole house?—*A snail.*

What runs round and round a tree and never gets tired?
—*The bark.*

There are two little windows in one big house. Everybody looks
into them, but only one person looks out. What is that?
—*The two eyes.*

What has life only when people touch it?
—*A musical instrument.*

When does a fool appear the cleverest?—*When he keeps still.*

Why does a stork stand on one leg?
—*Because he lifts the other up.*

What's in the middle of Basel?—*The letter S.*

What do you find in all the cooking pots in Berne?—*Bottoms.*

[77]

DENMARK

What is rounder than an egg and longer than the road to church?—*A ball of yarn.*

When I wore my white frock, nobody would have me;
When I wore my green frock, nobody would have me;
When I wore my red frock, some would have me;
When I wore my black frock, all would have me.
    —*A cherry (in blossom, green, partly ripe, and ripe).*

What people live only from wind and water?—*Millers.*

What is it that men seldom eat without, but seldom eat alone?—*Salt.*

How can you put a hundred pounds of meal into two sacks so that each sack contains a hundred pounds?
    —*By putting one sack inside the other.*

A miller went into his mill, which has four corners. In every corner stood three sacks, on each sack lay three cats, and every cat had three kittens. How many feet were there in the mill?—*The miller's two feet. Cats have paws.*

What most resembles a roast goose?—*A roast gander.*

Who can take a thousand men to town in one wagon?
    —*Anyone who will make enough trips.*

NORWAY

There was a man who was no man;
He went on a way that was no way;
He carried water without a pail.—*A rainbow.*

A tree stands on Reine:
It has twelve golden boughs,
Four nests on each bough
And seven eggs in each nest—
And the seventh is of gold.
—*The year: the months, weeks and days—including Sunday.*

What is the house full of white maidens with a red minstrel in
the middle?—*The mouth, teeth and tongue.*

What is the strongest animal?
              —*The snail, because it carries its house about.*

SWEDEN

Who lives on the waves and makes his living from the wind?
—*A fisherman.*

What is the sickle that no reaper can grind?—*The moon.*

I am one of the king's most distinguished guests: I eat his best dishes and then sit down on his nose and bite him.—*A fly.*

What goes uphill and downhill wearing twelve pairs of stockings on its back?—*A sheep.*

What goes uphill and downhill carrying a featherbed on its neck?—*A goose.*

What travels north, south, east and west, but goes neither on the ground nor in the air?—*A fish.*

Who is the world's greatest traveler?—*Money.*

LAPLAND

A man a hundred years old wears a hat that is only one day old. What is that?—*A tree covered with snow.*

A man fights a man: since he can never overpower him, he always has to retreat. What is that?
　　　　　　　　　　—A sea wave pounding against a rock.

What swallows flesh and blood at night and spits them out in the morning?—*A house.*

Two brothers go for a walk, and the big brother walks twelve miles while the little brother walks only one mile. What is that?—*The hands of a clock.*

What has neither hands nor feet but climbs high?
　　　　　　　　　　　　　　—Rising dough.

What is something that is and is not?—*A shadow.*

ICELAND

What is hairy inside and bald outside?—*A candle.*

A man runs forever without moving from his seat. He has no mouth or voice, yet he roars so loud that people hear him far away.—*It is a waterfall.*

Who is the boy that sleeps in the dirt and dies if he drinks water?—*Fire in a fireplace.*

Everybody can see that I exist, yet no one can find me—not even those who know how to use me.
                    —*The path of flight followed by birds.*

Tell me: what comes over the sea that will show a picture when asked and can imitate every creature?—*A mirror.*

If you want to become wise, turn me over on my back and open up my belly. What am I?—*A book.*

The Riddles of Odin

An old Icelandic saga tells that there was a king named Heidrik whose rule it was that a man could free himself from any sentence by asking riddles that King Heidrik could not answer. Once when the king was on bad terms with a great man named Gestumblindi, he ordered him to come and settle their differences through riddling at the Yuletide festival.

The god Odin took the form and appearance of Gestumblindi and came in his stead. In the king's great hall, he asked Heidrik many riddles, including the following:

> Four walk,
> Four hang,
> Two show the way,
> Two ward off dogs,
> And one always hangs behind.

Heidrik said, "It is a cow. Her four legs walk, the four teats of her udder hang, her two ears show the way, her two horns ward off dogs, and her tail hangs behind."

With equal skill Heidrik answered all the other riddles, until Odin at last grew daring and asked:

> What did Odin speak into his son Baldur's ear
> Before he was burned on the funeral pyre?

Heidrik knew that only the god Odin himself could know the answer. By this riddle Heidrik recognized Odin and angrily threw his magic sword Tyrfing at him, but Odin took the form of a hawk and flew away.

FINLAND

A bear breaks out of his den and blows with every hair—
what is it?—*A snowstorm.*

What dances and plays the whole summer long, but hides its
face when winter comes?—*A lake. (Ice covers it in winter.)*

When somebody comes into the house, who goes first to him
to ask the news?—*The dog.*

What gets dressed up three times a day, but goes naked most
of the time?—*The dining table.*

An old bald man keeps chasing five little brothers who run
ahead of him, but he never catches up with them. What is
that?—*The heel and toes of a foot.*

There are four narrow bays between five long peninsulas,
with a rock on the end of each. What is that?—*A hand.*

Thousands stand bowing to each other thousands and thousands of times. What is that?—*A field of wheat.*

What lies down on the ground but stands up in the water?
—*A fishing net.*

Two ships sail eternally across the sea, but they never meet each other. What are they?—*The sun and the moon.*

What is the great old chest with a new cover, that is opened only once a year?—*The frozen sea.*

What is stronger than fire?—*Water.*

What is stronger than water?—*Wind.*

ESTONIA

Who sits on the edge of the world, clothed in a robe of silk and gold?—*A rainbow.*

What bridge is built without any stone or wood?—*Ice.*

What mother is always devouring her children?
                    —*The sea. (Her children are the rivers.)*

Men are chopping trees in a far-off land and the chips fall here.—*Thunder and lightning.*

The earth is covered with little bullets, yet nobody is out hunting.—*Hailstones.*

What is it that everybody enjoys and everyone must have, yet everybody fears?—*Fire.*

What may you find in a wall that nobody put there?—*Cracks.*

What is it that all the people in the world do at the same time?—*They grow older.*

With one I am uncomfortable; I am just right for two; and I am too large for three. What am I?—*A secret.*

LITHUANIA

A dog barks and barks, then it runs behind the door: what is that?—*The tongue.*

What goes away on six feet and comes back on three?
—*A soldier rides away to war on a horse and returns home with a cane.*

When they drink from the trough, the trough makes noises. What is that?—*A sow feeding her pigs and grunting to them.*

What grows and grows without eating?—*Ice in winter.*

I break the ice and find silver;
I break the silver and find gold.—*An egg.*

HUNGARY

Young gentlemen are jumping all over the roads. What are they?—*Frogs.*

What has no feet or hands yet climbs to the ceiling?—*Smoke.*

A queen sits in her chair wearing a white gown, and her tears fall in her lap.—*A candle.*

Its belly is a boat,
Its foot is a paddle,
Its throat is a trumpet.—*A goose.*

A little house has two bright windows, that are opened every morning and closed every night.—*The eyes.*

An iron colt neighs on a meadow of bone.—*A razor shaving.*

What animal has its bones on the outside?—*The snail.*

I have a lock that not even the gypsies are good enough blacksmiths to make. What is it?—*An eggshell.*

Hungarian Gypsies

"My mother deserted me before I was born." Who is that?
—*A cuckoo.* (*Cuckoo mothers lay their eggs to hatch in the nests of other birds.*)

Who is the little man with a big hat on, standing in the woods? You eat the hat and throw the man away.

—*A mushroom.*

What is the black cow that neither eats nor drinks, yet feeds everybody?—*The earth.*

There is a mother whose milk delights everybody: she wears a wooden coat and iron corset stays.—*A wine keg.*

How many steps does a sparrow take in a day?

—*None. A sparrow* hops.

A forest grows everywhere. Men chop it down again and again, especially on Sundays and holidays, but every tree springs up again.—*The beard.*

CZECHOSLOVAKIA

It has cities, but no houses;
It has forests, but no trees;
It has rivers, but no fish.
What is it?—*A map.*

What is small and black, and if you touch it you say, "Ouch!"?
—A *thorn.*

What can fall into a well without even rippling the water?
—*Sunlight.*

I'm green, but I'm not grass;
I'm yellow, but I'm not an orange;
I have a tail, but I'm not a dog.—*A carrot.*

What runs and runs, trembling, and carries a white handkerchief in its hand?—*Foam on the water.*

BULGARIA

What weaves without a loom—it weaves and weaves but always remains naked?—*A spider.*

Ten priests wear tall hats on their heads. Who are they?
—*Fingers and nails.*

There are three bulls:
One eats and never gets full,
One lies down and never gets rested,
One flies away and never returns.—*Fire, ashes and smoke.*

What has a black skin and a white heart?—*A chestnut.*

The whole meadow is covered with water, yet the little ants keep running about. How can that be?—*The water is dew.*

Who works like a maid during the day, but sits up like a lady at night?—*The broom.*

What has no hoe, yet plows and digs in the ground?—*A mole.*

Before his father was born, the son had already gone to war. What is that?—*Fire and smoke.*

POLAND

A beautiful girl lost her earrings while playing in the meadow.
The moon left them there, but the sun came and picked them
up.—*Dewdrops.*

I have neither body nor soul, but when I play on my flute
everything starts moving. What is it?—*The wind.*

A quick knight walks along the stream, and when the little
friends see him they all run away.—*A stork and frogs.*

There are fields beyond measure
And cattle beyond counting;
Horned is the shepherd,
And rich is the landlord.
        —*The sky, the stars, the moon and the sun.*

How could you patch one hole with two other holes?
        —*By putting your nose in your mouth.*

Which is the shortest month?—*May. (It has only three letters.)*

What does every pig have that even God doesn't have?
        —*An owner.*

RUSSIA

Simple Ivan and the Princess

Once a tsar announced that his daughter wanted to marry a man clever at riddles. If a man asked riddles she could guess, he must have his head cut off, but the one who asked riddles she could not solve was to marry her. Many tried and failed, and lost their heads, and at last a poor peasant boy, Simple Ivan, decided to try.

On the way to the palace he saw a horse eating growing grain in a field. He drove it out with his whip and said, "That makes a riddle!" A little later he killed a snake with his spear and said, "That makes another riddle!"

At the palace, he asked his first riddle:

As I came here I saw a good thing;
In that good thing there was a good thing;
I drove the good thing from the good thing with a good
   thing;
And the good thing ran from the good thing out of the
   good thing.

The princess could not solve this, nor find the answer in

any riddle book. She sent a servant to try to buy the answer from Simple Ivan, but in vain. So at last she had to let Ivan explain that the three "good things" were the field of grain, the horse and the whip.

Then he asked his second riddle:
As I came here I saw a bad thing;
I struck the bad thing with a bad thing;
And the bad thing killed the bad thing.

When the princess failed also to answer this one, he explained that the two "bad things" were the snake and his spear. The princess was very angry that a simple peasant boy had out-witted her with riddles, but at last she had to admit herself defeated. So they were married and lived very happily.
                    —*Adapted from a popular Russian folktale.*

Fire burns in the middle of the sea,
And smoke comes out through the roof.—*A samovar.*

Grandfather has no ax, but he builds and builds and builds everything solid. What is that?—*Frost.*

What can open gates without having arms or hands?
                                        —*The wind.*

A little watchdog is curled up at the door:
It can't bark and it can't bite,
But it keeps you out of the house.—*The lock.*

What do I have that you have, the Pope has and every fish in the sea has?—*A name.*

What is it that makes two people out of one?—*A mirror.*

What is it that sees nothing yet shows the road to others?
                                                —*A road sign.*

What smokes but isn't a man, and weaves but isn't a woman?
                                                —*A textile factory.*

What is in the middle of the Volga?—*The letter L.*

What kind of a bush does a rabbit sit under when it rains?
                                                —*A wet one.*

What walks above us with its feet upside down?
                                        —*A fly on the ceiling.*

What baby is born with a beard?—*A baby goat.*

What baby is born with a moustache?—*A baby cat.*

Votiak Tribe

Who is she who walks through the sky in clothes of many
colors?—*The rainbow.*

A bear and a wolf glare into each other's eyes. What is that?
                        —*The window and the door of a house.*

If you look on one side of your hand, they are there.
But if you look on the other side, they are not there.
                                        —*Your fingernails.*

What goes away ugly and comes back pretty?—*The dirty wash.*

What is it that no one can lock up in a chest?—*Sunlight.*

He doesn't ask his father, he doesn't ask his mother, but he
goes straight up to heaven.—*Smoke.*

What can judge truly, though lifeless?—*Scales.*

YUGOSLAVIA

Fire burns on the snake's head, and the pasha kisses its tail.
What is that?—*Someone smoking a pipe.*

What goes over the mountains talking to the mountains, and
goes over the water talking to the water?—*Sound.*

What calls to others but cannot hear itself call?—*A bell.*

A little red pot boils in the middle of the field:
No one takes it off, and no one tends the fire.—*An ant hill.*

What is empty in the daytime and full at night?—*A bed.*

If I am young I stay young, but if I am old I stay old. What
is that?—*A portrait.*

The tsar reaches heaven, and the tsarina reaches only to the
tsar's knees. What is that?—*Smoke and fire.*

ALBANIA

What runs day and night and never gets tired?—*A river.*

What runs away and never looks back?—*A bullet.*

A thousand thousand knots;
A thousand thousand holes.—*A fishing net.*

A thousand sisters drink water at the same time. What is that?—*The roof tiles (when it rains).*

A sister grabs her brother round the neck. What is that?
—*A buttonhole and button.*

What has flesh on both sides and wood in the middle?
—*A team of oxen and the wagon tongue.*

What has wood on both sides and flesh in the middle?
—*A cradle with a baby in it.*

A son beats his father and the father rouses everybody within hearing. What is that?—*The clapper strikes the bell in a tower.*

GREECE

A little snake swallows the lake,
And then the lake swallows the snake.
>*—The wick and oil of a lamp.*

A red monastery with black monks inside: what is it?
>*—A watermelon with black seeds.*

A round tower loaded with cannon: what is it?
>*—A hedgehog.*

Without as smooth as glass,
Within a woolly mass;
But hid amid the wool
There lurks a nice mouthful.—*A chestnut.*

An ivory garden with a singing nightingale: what is it?
                                        —*The teeth and tongue.*

Five grab it, thirty-two hammers break it; then a maiden embraces it and sends it down!—*It is food.*

What has a voice like a bagpipe, and has neither hair nor tail?—*A frog.*

The Riddle of the Sphinx

According to Greek mythology, the city of Thebes was punished in a fearful way for neglecting its duties to the gods. A dreadful Sphinx was sent to dwell on a rock outside the city, and of every passerby she asked a riddle:

> What is it that has a name and goes on four
> feet, on two feet and on three feet?

The Sphinx killed and ate all who could not answer correctly, and Thebes could not be free of her until the riddle was answered. Countless young men lost their lives by giving wrong solutions.

Finally, King Creon offered the Theban throne and his daughter Jocasta in marriage to the one who could solve the riddle. Then young Oedipus appeared, heard the riddle and said, "It is man. As a baby he crawls on all fours; when grown he walks upright on two feet; but in old age he carries a staff as a third foot."

Upon hearing the answer, the Sphinx threw herself angrily from the rock and was killed.

TURKEY

I have many children and they get a bath every day. What is that?—*Spoons.*

What is this: a block with seven holes? He who can't guess it is a blockhead!—*The head.* (*The holes are the eyes, ears, nostrils and mouth.*)

There is marble below and marble above, and in the middle dances a red woman. What is that?—*The teeth and tongue.*

Grass grows everywhere in Istanbul. The oftener it is cut the faster it grows. What is that?—*Hair on people's heads.*

I have a turban which, unwound, has no end. What is it?
—*A road.*

ISRAEL

There was a king who ruled no people:
He sailed a ship in the middle of the sea;
He sent a messenger without a letter,
And got an answer that was not written.
          —*Noah, the ark, the dove, and the olive branch.*

Everybody loves me forever, but nobody can look into my face.—*The sun.*

Who are the parents who lived long ago? They had few children but thousands of grandchildren—yet they themselves had no parents.—*Adam and Eve.*

Twin sisters are swinging in a swing: when one goes up the other comes down. What is that?—*A balance scale.*

When was one-fourth of all mankind killed in one struggle?
                                    —When Cain killed Abel.

I spread a net but I'm not a fisherman;
What I catch in the net is not a fish.

                                    —A spider and a fly.

I'm not an airplane but I fly in the sky;
I'm not a river but I'm full of water.—*A cloud.*

The Boy and the Astrologers

A king once decided to build a city and chose a site. The astrologers approved of the place on condition that a child be walled in alive, brought voluntarily by its mother. After three years a mother brought a child, about ten years old.

When ready to be walled in, the boy said to the king, "Let me ask the astrologers three questions. If they answer correctly, then they have read the signs aright. But if not, they must have been mistaken."

The king granted the request, and the boy asked, "What is the lightest thing, what is the sweetest thing, and what is the hardest thing in the world?"

After three days the astrologers replied, "The lightest thing in the world is a feather, the sweetest is honey, and the hardest is stone."

The young boy laughed and said, "Anybody could answer like that! The lightest thing in the world is an only child in its mother's arms; it is never heavy. The sweetest is a mother's milk to a baby. And the hardest is for a mother to bring her child willingly to be buried alive in a wall."

The astrologers were confounded and had to own that they had read the stars wrongly. And the child was saved.

                                    —A Jewish folktale.

AFRICA

A Hausa Riddle Story

Once a chief told his three sons to mount their horses and show him which of them had the greatest skill. The eldest son charged at a baobab tree, drove his spear through it and then rode his horse through the hole he had made. The second son grabbed up his horse by the bridle and jumped with it over the top of the same tree. Then the third son pulled the baobab tree up by the roots and rode up to his father, waving the tree over his head in the air. Who excelled among them?
—*There is no answer* (*to such a big fib*).

A Loma Riddle Story from Liberia

Three men went hunting and one shot at a rock. The shot went through the rock and killed an elephant. The second man followed the shot through the rock and carried the elephant back through the hole. The third man caught a louse in his hair, skinned it and sewed up the elephant in the louse's skin. Which of the three did the biggest stunt?
—*There is no answer.*

EGYPT

What is this: the Pasha with his soldiers stands on a blue plate strewn with pearls—God help anyone who tries to count them.—*The moon, the sky and the stars.*

A ship with creaking sails comes from Arabia, bearing a little slave who will moisten the whole land.
   —*The ship is thunder and the little slave is a rain cloud.*

What is the cloth woven without thread that conquers both Turks and Sultans?—*Sleep.*

What is as big as a slice of bread and disappears into a drawer as soon as it goes to the bazaar?—*A twenty-piaster piece (a large gold coin).*

What is whiter than cotton, blacker than coal, higher than a minaret and lower than a wooden shoe?
                                        —*Black and white doves.*

What is only a span wide and carries a camel's load?—*A shoe.*

What is deaf and dumb and blind, yet knows what is in one's heart?—*A writing reed.*

You eat something that you neither plant nor plow:
It is the son of water, but if water touches it it dies.—*Salt.*

What did I buy with my money that I could not bring home with me?—*A ship.*

What needs no head to dive into the water?
                                        —*A well-bucket.*

What is the most beautiful day?
                    —*The day when one makes money.*

What is softer than cream cheese and sharper than a sword?
                                        —*A snake.*

ALGERIA

A Sultan in glittering garments has just arrived. The wise ones have gone to meet him, while the foolish ones have covered up their heads. Who is he?—*The dawn.* (*The "wise ones" are at work; the "foolish ones" have gone back to sleep.*)

O learned man, if you can reveal hidden truths, tell me: What may a man have in his skin that God did not put there?—*Tattooing.*

Crooked as a sickle, he is not made of steel;
Heaped up like a straw pile, he is not made of straw;
Tall as an almond tree, he is not a tree.—*A camel.*

What grows and grows: even when you cut off its head it does not die?—*Your fingernail.*

What walks on six legs and flies with four wings? It eats up a whole land and then goes far away.—*A locust.*

It helps you to understand, but you can't see it.
You can grab it, but you can't carry it off. What is it?
                                                    —*Your ear.*

What is always smaller than its mother and bigger than its father?—*A mule.*

[107]

I passed by a remarkable village where all the men were
singing and the women were quiet. What could that be?
—*Roosters and hens in a chickenyard.*

A stone came from the river, that isn't a stone;
It has four legs, and isn't a goat;
It lays eggs, and it isn't a fowl.—*A turtle.*

ABYSSINIA

What is the black ox that bellows with its nose in the earth?
—*A plow.*

What is that crumb in the middle of a huge basket with a huge lid on top?
—*Man.* (*The basket is the earth and the lid the sky.*)

Going to the field they say, "Homewards!" Coming home they say, "To the field!" What are they?—*A goat's horns.*

A little black errand boy runs busily up and down the road all day. Who is he?—*An ant.*

A strange marvel occurred: an egg blossomed on a bush!
—*A cotton boll opened.*

What is it that you don't have to sharpen, because it is already sharp?—*A thorn.*

What bellows like a lion, yet you carry it about like a dead thing?—*A gun.*

What hops up and down when you shut it up in its house?
—*Soup boiling in a pot with the lid on.*

What sprouts in the sunshine and is mown down in water?
—*The beard.*

AFRICAN TRIBES

Tonga

What tiny creature weighs so heavily that you wouldn't like to carry it to town?—*A mosquito.*

What swallows people at sundown?—*Their huts.*

A hen sits over a fire with her tail dancing in the air. What is that?—*A pot boiling.*

I don't live outside—I live in the water. What is that?
                                        —*A hippopotamus.*

I took my ox to market and it came back home with me. What is it?—*My shadow.*

What is the well where water always comes out?
                                        —*A cow's nose. (It is never dry.)*

Who are the girls who play even in the thorn bushes?
                                        —*Raindrops.*

Baiga

A boy dances, and as he dances he ties a white turban on his head.—*It is corn popping.*

Nandi

I met a woman carrying something that looked like a man's head. What was it?—*A pumpkin.*

If I see a person coming toward me, I kick dust into his eyes, I escape. What am I?—*A flea.*

Zulu

Guess, who are the men, adorned in white hip-dresses, lined up in a row to dance the wedding dance?—*The teeth.*

What man is that whose laughter causes men and trees and grass to weep?—*Fire.*

Kxatla

Tell me: The children are dancing but their mother does not dance.—*The branches on a tree.*

Tell me: White goats that descend from the mountain.
                    —*Hail falls from the sky.*

Tell me: The guinea fowl that stands on one leg. Its thigh is very tasty.—*A mushroom.*

Tell me: Baboon, squat on your haunches, so that the children can rejoice.—*A cooking pot set on the fire.*

[111]

Tell me: The red bull which bellows louder than all the others. —*The tongue.*

Tell me: The two pythons which are lying side by side.
—*Wagon tracks.*

Tell me: Five hyenas which go into the same hole.
—*The fingers. (The "hole" is a glove.)*

Tell me: The little red calf that fills the houses of the white people.—*A lamp.*

Chaga

Who is the chief over the whole world?—*The sun.*

I know a pasture; on it are five trees.—*It is the hand.*

There is a mountain which trembles.
—*It is the hump on a buffalo bull.*

The small one conquers the large one.
—*The ax cuts down the tree.*

The chief lives in the middle of the country.
—*The tongue and mouth.*

If you are too greedy, you eat yourself.
—*Don't bite your tongue!*

Makua

When I visited my friend and porridge was stirred for me, who rushed first to eat it?—*A fly.*

There is something that we carry every day. It is a big thing and heavy besides. What is it?—*The head.*

My mother's chicken lies among thorns: what is that?
                                        —*The tongue (and teeth).*

I have two reed mats: I sleep on one and the other hangs over me. What are they?—*The earth and the sky.*

Hausa

How does a woman walk?—*Like a pumpkin.*

A thousand oxen are going along and they raise no dust. What is that?—*A column of ants.*

A small trading woman goes to market in the world below. What is that?—*A bucket goes down the well.*

I have given you food; why do you still look at me? What is that?—*A dog.*

MADAGASCAR

Standing erect it looks at heaven; stooping down it sees only the footprints of oxen. What is it?—*Rice growing.*

What is dead before it begins to bluster?
                                        —*A drum (made of cowhide).*

There is earth under the person;
The person is under dry grass;
The dry grass is under water;
The water is surrounded by earth.
—*A water carrier. An earthen water pot sits on his head on a grass head pad.*

What is God's little bag with invisible stitching?—*An egg.*

Something has many shields and spears, yet it cannot protect its wife and children.—*A lemon tree. (It has thorns, but people gather the fruit.)*

What is the honor of the forest?—*The* laingo *vine.*

What is the perfume of the forest?—*The ginger tree.*

What is the fat of the forest?—*The honeycomb.*

[115]

MAURITIUS

Along the path I saw a crowd of girls, all hanging their heads. What is that?—*A grove of banana trees.*

I bought many slaves in the market, but when I got them home I worked only one of them at a time. What did I buy?
                                        —*A package of needles.*

I throw it into the air and it falls to the ground;
I throw in on the ground and it goes up into the air.
                                        —*A rubber ball.*

Who is the girl standing in the road? Everybody that passes kisses her.—*A fountain.*

Who goes everywhere at night, but in the daytime hangs with her head down and her feet sticking up?—*A bat.*

What is the pool that overflows if the tiniest straw falls into it?—*The eye.*

"You grab it while I go for more!" What is that?—*It is what the hand says to the mouth while eating.*

What tongue never tells a lie?—*An animal's tongue.*

ASIA & OCEANIA

The Riddle of the Air Castle

An old Arabian story includes a famous and curious riddle. The pharaoh of Egypt sent a message to the king of Assyria, saying that the king would have to pay tribute to Egypt unless he could explain how a castle came to be built in air.

The frightened king sent his wise vizier Haikar to Egypt, where the pharaoh asked him the following riddle:

An architect built a castle in the air, using 8,760 stones. He planted in it twelve trees, each with thirty branches, and on each branch a black and white bunch of grapes. What is that?

Haikar said, "The riddle means the year and its divisions. The trees are the months, the branches are the days in a month, the black and white grapes are day and night, and the number 8,760 is the number of hours in a year."

The pharaoh loaded him with treasure for solving the riddle and he returned to Assyria, where the king greeted him with great joy.

ARABIA

Once I ran pleasantly through a valley, but if you want to avoid pain don't touch me now. What is that?—*Boiling water.*

There is a wonderful thing: its dress is sweetness, its body wood. What is it?—*A date.*

What is as big as an elephant, yet small as a folded table-cloth?—*A mosquito net.*

A lady sits weeping in the window, and her tears will finally destroy her. What is that?—*A burning candle.*

A ship comes full of slaves, each with a stick on his head. What is that?—*A shipload of raisins.*

A man rides two camels, who never get tired and who let no one else ride them. What is that?—*A man wearing shoes.*

PERSIA

Who is the king that travels with thousands of shining knights—
yet when another knight appears alone with a yellow banner,
the king and all his followers flee?

> —*The moon and stars, and the sun.*

What is the city that is peopled by lifeless men? In time of
war you see it very active and prosperous, but in time of
peace it is deserted and desolate.—*A chess board.*

Two black and white doves are tied in separate nests, and they
fly to the sky without leaving their nests.—*The eyes.*

What is that good elegant body that even handsome people
eat? It is shaped like the dome of a minaret, and wears red
and white clothing. Whoever kills it must weep over it.

> —*An onion.*

I saw a silvery snake with a golden bird in its mouth, lying
in a round cistern. The snake was drinking the water and
the water was eating the snake. When the snake drank up all
the water, the golden bird died.—*An oil lamp. (The snake is
the wick, the water is the oil and the golden bird is the flame.)*

Who is that shining beauty with whom everybody is in love?
Whoever is lucky enough to win her can have everything
he wants.—*Money.*

Persian Dervishes

What is light as a fairy and flies roaring through the air—
though it has neither wings nor a mouth?
—*A kite. (It has an opening for the wind to roar through.)*

What is that fairy shape that has no life? It laughs yet has no
mouth, it weeps yet has no eyes, and it travels far and wide
yet has no feet.—*A cloud.*

What is it that no one has ever seen, yet it travels to the sky
ahead of the eye?—*Sight.*

A man from Africa came to me with the strangest animal God
ever created. Its head was like eighty heads, its belly like ten
bellies and its legs like thirty legs. What was it?—*An elephant.*

INDIA

Bengal

Two are standing up,
Two are flapping,
Four are walking
And two are flashing.—*An ox: horns, ears, legs and eyes.*

What animal can swallow its own head?—*A turtle.*

What is the cowshed full of cows with all their horns pointing
down?—*A bunch of bananas.*

What has two horns when young, loses them in youth and
regains them in old age?—*The moon.*

If anyone can catch it I will give him a thousand rupees.
What is it?—*The wind.*

It lives in the water and is not a fish;
It wags two horns and is not a buffalo.
What is it?—*A snail.*

While the Raja's son sits eating rice, his two sons stare at him.
What is that?—*The two knees sticking up.*

Parsee

What golden parrot drinks with its tail?—*An oil lamp.*

Who is the stunted little slave that can make a whole village weep?—*A chili pepper.*

Two seize me and carry me to two caves. What is that? —*Snuff (carried by thumb and finger to nostrils).*

Where there is a village there are no people, and where there is a river there is no water. Where is that?—*On a map.*

What jar holds two kinds of butter?—*An egg.*

What runs fast with a thousand people in it?—*A train.*

It is white but is not sugar,
It is bright but is not glass,
It melts but is not snow:
And you eat it every day.—*Salt.*

Santal

A little Santal boy runs all around a hill. What is he?
—*A razor.*

Below the thicket a glistering;
Below the glistering a foaming;
Below the foaming a chattering.
What is that?—*The hair, eyes, nose and mouth.*

What runs into the earth in the morning and doesn't come
out again until noon?—*A plow.*

Who stands dumb until he is slapped—then he speaks out?
—*A drum.*

Who drinks water through his nose?—*An elephant.*

"Come along, you five brothers! Push me past the white
stones." Who is speaking?—*Rice. (He is telling the fingers
to put it into the mouth.)*

Kashmir

"Oh, father, I fell down! Oh, mother, I fell down! And as soon
as I fell down a calf ate me." What is that?
—*A leaf fallen from a tree.*

Silver branches stretched across a golden ceiling. Wise said
to Witty, "Who tied them?" What is that?—*A spider's web.*

A smooth bed has been spread, yet nobody sleeps there.
What is it?—*Ice on water.*

The children are gods but their mother is a devil. What is that?—*Roses on a thorny bush.*

Black crows sit on a white bank and say, "Caw, caw!" What is that?—*Writing on paper.*

I shot an arrow into the sky, which went all the way to Hindustan.—*I sent a letter.*

There is something to eat,
Something to drink,
Something to gnaw on,
Something for the cow to eat,
And something to sow in the garden!
Yet it is only one thing.—*A watermelon.*

What stands up without support?—*The sky.*

What has no covering?—*The river.*

Who will wash the jungle?—*Snow and rain.*

Who will sweep the jungle?—*Wind.*

The Goat and the Boys

In a Panjabi legend, the Raja Rasalu, among many adventures, visits the kingdom of the Raja Sirikap, who entertains the visitor and offers to give him a white-covered coach if he can ask a riddle which Sirikap cannot answer. Rasalu asked the following double riddle:

[125]

Within your city boundary,
A wonder I did note:
A horse and sixty villages
Were swallowed by a goat.

Then came a bald-headed urchin,
Of most capacious maw,
Who stooped him down and guzzled up
The Ravi and Chenab.

The riddle described two things which Rasalu had seen along the road. First he saw a discharged old soldier washing clothes on a river bank, who had received, as his reward, a paper granting him a horse and the income from sixty villages. The paper was tied up in his turban, and when the soldier's back was turned, a stray goat came along and ate up turban and paper.

Next he saw two boys playing. One formed a small pool of water and said, "This is the river Ravi." The other formed another pool and said, "This is the river Chenab." Just then a shaven-headed third boy came, who stooped down and drank up the water out of both pools.

Since the Raja Sirikap could not solve the riddle, he had to give the white-covered coach to the Raja Rasalu.

CEYLON

What tree stands by the door? It has twenty branches and twenty little strips of bark—one on each branch. Twenty raps on the head of anyone who can't guess that!
—*A person: the branches are fingers and toes and the bark strips are the fingernails and toenails.*

What cries out on this bank of the river and drops down on the other?—*A bullet.*

On the upper shoot there are five hundred songsters;
On the lower shoot there are five hundred songsters;
Between them is an infant of divine beauty.
Whoever can solve this will become a Buddha.
                    —*The eye. (Eyelids, lashes and the eye itself.)*

Long like a creeper,
Beautiful like a flower,
Of royal caste,
And with a deadly bite.—*The cobra.*

The leaf is beautifully enchased;
The flower is worked with red thread;
And in three months it grows as big as a chicken.
The one who can solve this deserves a country.
                    —*The pineapple.*

SIAM

Closed it's the size of a bamboo tube, but opened it's the
size of a winnowing basket. What is it?—*An umbrella.*

What hums like a bumblebee and walks about on one foot?
—*A top.*

An old Chinese man with a bent body goes into the water without muddying it. What is it?—*A fish hook.*

What comes from China that has a very small body and a very loud voice?—*A firecracker.*

It's as black as a flea: the more it is struck the more it bites, and the more it bites the more it is struck. What is it.—*A nail.*

What comes walking on four feet and has a tiled roof?
—*A turtle.*

What is it that wears a white skirt as a child, a green wrapper in youth and a red one when old?—*A chili pepper.*

What has bones instead of a skin, and two eyes but no head? It travels about in the water, but shelters in the earth.
—*A crab.*

What is this: the more it is worn, the newer it becomes; but if you keep it put away, the older it becomes.
—*It is knowledge.*

A half coconut that can cross over the sea—what is it?
—*The half moon.*

There's a whole thicket of bamboo, in which no stalk is jointed. What is it?—*The hair.*

MALAYA

What fruit is shaped like the great clapper of a gong, and its leaves are like swords?—*The pineapple.*

Who goes into the water carrying a curtain?
                              —A fisherman with his net.

What moves away from you when you pull it with a rope, and moves nearer you when you let its rope go?—*The sail on a boat.*

What goes into the mill wet and comes out dry?—*Sugar cane.*

What has soft silky hair in youth and dry brittle hair in old age?—*An ear of corn.*

What child keeps pounding its mother?
                       —The pestle (which pounds the mortar).

What sleeps all day and cries all night?—*A cricket.*

What is it that is a snake and isn't a snake?
                       —A snake's skin that it sloughs off.

Where can you find a spring that never gets muddied?
                              —The milk in a coconut.

ANNAM

Our country has a tree:
On top it is a basket,
Its root is thin as a toothpick,
And its leaves fly away to China.—*A box-shaped kite.*

What is the tree without branches where two children are
swinging?—*A cornstalk with two ears of corn.*

I beg fire from the *genie* in the kitchen;
Then I light a dragon's head, and thunder rumbles,
And the dragon flies away through the air.
                    —*Smoking a large tobacco pipe.*

Five men with two sticks drive white herons into a cave. What
is that?—*Eating rice with chopsticks.*

They have round bodies and a white skin: right after dinner
they get their faces washed and all go to bed together. What
are they?—*The family's rice bowls.*

What is the house, yellow inside and outside, that no stranger
dares to enter?—*A beehive.*

At night a mother has thousands of sons, who all die at
daybreak. Then a deathless old man appears; he is so fearful
that nobody can bear to look at him.
                    —*It is the moon and stars, and the sun.*

CHINA

What is the big rooster who bows to everyone it sees?
                                                          —The teapot.

Far away you see mountains in clouds.
Listen! there is water—but it makes no sound.
The flowers never move when the wind blows,
Nor do the birds fly away when you draw near.
                              —It is a Chinese landscape painting.

Needles fall from the sky, but you can't find them!
                                                          —Rain falls.

Green bamboos tied together fly over high mountains.
They like a high wind, but they are afraid of rain.
                    —A kite. (Rain would destroy the paper.)

In a lumpy house a fat little white baby sleeps under a red
mosquito net.—*A peanut.*

A pig walks along a wall, taking a bite at every step.
                                                    —Scissors cutting.

What is cleaner without washing—washing only makes it dirtier?—*Water.*

Ge-li-ge-da, weave up;
Ge-li-ge-da, weave down;
Ge-li-ge-da, weave knots;
Ge-li-ge-da, the knots are woven.—*A net.*

There is a general in your family:
He stands up straight, upon a thousand feet;
He works for you daily without ever groaning;
He drives thousands of devils out of your house.—*A broom.*

Someone is clothed with heavy armor;
His eyes stick out like two iron balls.
You would think him to be a hero,
Yet he always marches sideways, never forward.—*A crab.*

There is a giant dragon: He is hard on top and always hungry, though he eats no solid food; suddenly he dashes forward, roaring ferociously and leaving a trail of smoke.
                                        —*An automobile.*

You look like my twin, but I can speak and you cannot.
                                        —*Reflection in a mirror.*

How can you add ten to ten and still have ten?
                                        —*Put on gloves.*

Two white plaster walls, and between them a red beauty: what is it?—*An egg.*

MONGOLIA

A golden camel opens its mouth,
And suddenly the rope flashes!—*Lightning*.

Inside a big house there's a small house;
Inside the small house there's a fat little boy.
                    —*A boot, a sock and a foot.*

A whole piece of silk that cannot be rolled up;
Ten thousand pearls that cannot be strung.
                    —*The sky and the stars.*

A Chinese goat yelled once and died: what is that?
                    —*A china dish broke.*

A sorrel horse behind a fence of birch trees: what is that?
                    —*The tongue and teeth.*

A small bird bows and bows its head;
It drinks from the middle of the river,
And walks in the pasture, making patterns, patterns.
                    —*Writing with a brush.*

A gray horse jumped up and the skies thundered: what is
that?—*Firing a gun.*

An envoy in a black jacket comes singing from the Emperor's country. He sits down and strokes his beard.—*A fly*.

The iron pig has a tail of string: what is that?
                              —*A needle and thread*.

What cow has no calf?—*The ox*.

What water has no fish?—*Well water*.

TIBET

What is the flaming golden flower?—*A fire blazing.*

Two sons are beating their father, and the father cries out so loudly that everybody hears, but nobody is sorry for him. Instead, the people are all very happy. What is that?
>—*Two drumsticks are beating a drum at a festival.*

If you tie him up he runs, but if you untie him and set him free he stands still. What is that?—*A shoe.*

What is it that can go instantly to the sky without flying or running or even stepping out through the door?
>—*A glance of an eye.*

It bellows like an ox in its cave; you often see it, but it never comes outside; nobody asks it to fetch or carry, but you always remember it at mealtime. What is it?—*The tongue.*

What is white-headed when it is born?—*An egg.*

SIBERIA

Yakut Tribe

When does everybody in the world speak the same language?
—*When they are babies crying.*

Who carries a tree on his head?—*A deer.*

Old men go into the house and their bald heads stick outside the house. What is that?—*Buttons and buttonholes.*

What is only an inch long and has a tail a mile long?
—*A needle and thread.*

Who are they who dress themselves in the summer and undress in the winter?—*Trees.*

Who rides a cow?—*An insect.*

What has no tongue, but talks about everything?—*A book.*

KOREA

What is the dead tree that stands up and moves?
—*A boat mast.*

What is the red silk purse that contains hundreds of gold coins?—*A red pepper.*

What is like a golden flame in an azure field?—*A star.*

What gets bathed three times a day?—*Dishes.*

What carries its load all day and all night?—*A shelf.*

What has a fat stomach whether it eats or not?—*A cooking pot.*

What stands in the field with its hair disheveled?
—*Corn on the stalk.*

What is like a cow but has no horns?—*A calf.*

What is most like the right hip?—*The left hip.*

JAPAN

What wears many kimonos when a child, but is naked when grown?—*A bamboo plant.*

What is this: There's a sweetshop inside a lumber shop inside a leather shop inside a thorn shop?—*A chestnut.*

What is the resemblance between women planting rice and boys writing with pens?
                    —*Both are dirty when they leave their work.*

Why are a bat and a street lamp lighter alike?
                              —*Both move about at nightfall.*

In what way is a morning glory like a newspaper?
                        —*We see them both in the morning.*

What is the resemblance between cherry blossom buds and an important letter?—*It is hard to wait for both to be open.*

What is the resemblance between an autumn sky and poorly dyed cloth?—*Both change color easily.*

Why is a train like a postman with a pipe?

> —*Each goes along puffing smoke.*

What has six legs but walks with only four?

> —*A man on horseback.*

How does the moon resemble a bald head?

> —*Both are round and shine.*

PHILIPPINE ISLANDS

I planted a calabash vine that can reach from here to Manila. What is that?—*A telegraph line.*

What has a tail when little, but none when grown?—*A frog.*

What creature that God made always sleeps with its head hanging down?—*A bat.*

What is taller sitting down than standing up?—*A dog.*

What claps and claps, yet the neighbors never hear?
—*The eyelids.*

A sweet lady is surrounded by thorns. What is that?
—*A pineapple.*

I cannot see though my eyes are wide open, but if I cover them I see. What is that?—*Wearing spectacles.*

"If you carry me, I will carry you." Who is speaking?—*Shoes.*

Who are the four friends that have existed since time began?
—*The four directions.*

What runs without having feet, and roars without having a mouth?—*The sea.*

There is a flying thing:
It has the neck of a cow,
The chest of a man,
Wings like bamboo leaves,
A tail like a snake's,
And feet like a bird's.
What is it?—*A grasshopper*.

JAVA

There are two flowers: when they bloom they fill the whole world.—*The sun and the moon.*

What walks on three legs and sees with four eyes?
—*An old man with cane and spectacles.*

A warrior passes by who can overturn the earth. He has ten legs and three heads. His left hand clings to a bow and his right hand carries a sharp arrow. What is that?
—*A plowman, team, plow and whip.*

What has four legs that it uses not for walking but for standing still?—*A chair.*

He goes everywhere, although he is blind, deaf and dumb. Yet a clever person needs only to look at him to understand him.—*It is a book.*

What has earth above and earth below?
—*A house with an earthen roof.*

A white box is full of gold and silver. What is that?—*An egg.*

FIJI ISLANDS

There is a chief: He has only to speak, and fowls and pigs and men fall down before him. What is it?—*A gun.*

Who are the twenty men that always wear white turbans?
—*The fingers and toes, with their nails.*

There is a box: Goods are continually poured into it, yet it is never full.—*It is the human mind.*

There is a land: If I squeeze it with my hand it is hidden; if I release it it is again a land.—*A sponge.*

There is a man who fills his whole house: Soon he will break it open, leap out and run away, leaving the house in ruins.
—*A chick in the egg.*

Two men fight every day all day long: They stop fighting only at night and begin all over again every morning.
—*They are the eyelids.*

Canoe Riddles

What stands erect all the way to Tonga?—*The mast.*

What spits and spits and spits, all the way to Tonga?
—*The canoe baler (used continually at sea).*

What dives in Fiji and comes up in Tonga?
—*The steering oar (not lifted until the journey ends).*

Two fish are feeding in the sea: One eats with two mouths and the other with only one.
—*The Fijian double canoe and the white man's boat.*

SAMOA

Who is the very tall slim man who always keeps his head-dress on?—*A palm tree with its fronds.*

Who is the strong man who lives in the sea? He has eight arms but no legs.—*The octopus.*

Who is the very small man who lives in a cave and rules over a boundless country? When he is good people become good, and when he is bad people become bad.—*The tongue.*

Who is the man that dwells in a house made of a net?
—*A spider.*

What is the tribe that lives in every country?—*Flies.*

A company of ten strong soldiers take care of their king. Who are they?—*The ten fingers; they work for the stomach.*

What is the beautiful useful house that has five entrances?
—*It is a man and his five senses.*

A man is made of gold and his dress is made of silver. What is that?—*An egg.*

HAWAII

At night you may see a great shellfish surrounded by many small shellfish. What are they?—*The moon and stars.*

I have a bird that walks on its beak. What is it?
                                            —*A spinning top.*

I have a little round box—the key that will open it is hidden inside.—*A bird's egg.*

What three walls must you go through to reach a fountain?
                                        —*The walls of a coconut.*

My double canoe has ten noses. What is it?
                                        —*The feet with ten toes.*

My small man goes to a distance, then beckons—*A wave.*

My little man has a loud voice.—*Thunder.*

My little hot fish: Bite the head and it is hot, bite the middle and it is hot, bite the tail and it is hot.—*An onion.*

In what place can you store food where rats can never find it?—*In your stomach.*

I have a box that never rattles when I open or close it.
                                            —*The eye.*

I have a lop-sided gourd hanging on a cliff: what is it?
—*The ear.*

My long house has two doors and only one post: what is it?
—*The nose.*

My little fish cannot be seasoned with salt: what is it?
—*The tongue.*

The End of Riddling*

"What stands on one leg, tucks its head under one wing and barks?"

"An ostrich!"

"How could an ostrich bark?"

"You just put that in to make it hard to guess."

"What is long and red and hangs on the wall and whistles?"

"I give up."

"A herring."

"Herrings aren't red!"

"I painted this one red."

"How could it be on a wall?"

"I hung it there."

"But herrings can't whistle."

"So it doesn't whistle!"

* These riddles are used in many countries to end a riddling game.

ACKNOWLEDGMENTS

Our largest single debt of gratitude is to Professor Archer Taylor of the University of California, whose comparative study, *English Riddles from Oral Tradition,* has guided us to many valuable sources. We are especially indebted to Professor Taylor and the University of California Press for permission to take from the above book and from Vernam E. Hull's and Professor Taylor's *A Collection of Welsh Riddles* all the riddles we print for Holland (except our first one), Hungary, Java and Wales (except Welsh Gypsies), and some of those for Greece. For Greece, Holland, Hungary and Java, we utilized Professor Taylor's translations from Polites, Joos, Hamizade and Ranneft, whose works are listed in the Bibliography of *English Riddles from Oral Tradition.* We are also indebted to Professor Taylor for the riddles from his great Mongolian collection. We have sometimes adapted these riddles for what we deemed to be easier understanding, but we hope we have not harmed them, in concept and beauty, by doing so.

To Professor David McAllester of Wesleyan University we are indebted for the Comanche Indian riddles, which he has generously allowed us to print in advance of their scholarly publication. Professor Taylor has called these, in a letter, "discoveries of the very first importance [since] the orthodox view is that American Indians do not have riddles."

To Mr. William J. Gedney and Mr. Chit Phumsak we are indebted for the unusual Siamese riddles, adapted from a collection of thirty-seven riddles supplied by Mr. Phumsak and translated by Mr. Gedney, mailed to us from Bankok, Thailand, in 1953. Very few Siamese riddles are known in English.

For a number of Chinese riddles we are indebted to Mrs. Vera Hsu of Evanston, Illinois, and to Mrs. Anna Wu Wikland and Mr. H. W. Li of New York. We are indebted to Miss Freda Lulinsky of New York for most of the Russian riddles. For most of the Peruvian riddles we are indebted to Dr. William Mangin of Syracuse University, who sent them to us in 1953, while doing anthropological fieldwork in Peru. We are indebted to Mr. Anthony Leeds of New York for many of the Brazilian riddles, from his anthropological field notes. Some of the riddles for the United States, Brazil and Cuba, and the Cuban riddle story, came from unpublished field notes of the senior editor. We owe a special debt to the distinguished folklorist Vance Randolph for many valuable suggestions as well as for some of the riddles for the United States, from the collections published by him and his collaborators.

We are also deeply grateful to Mr. Waldemar Syrkus of New York for translating from Hebrew the Israeli riddles, as well as many others from Slavic languages and German, often from archaic dialects.

We must let the following list of books and articles stand as grateful testimony to the rest—and major part—of our indebtedness.

SOURCES

Aarne, Antti. *Vergleichende Rätselforschungen,* I-III. FF Communications, XXVI-XXVIII. Helsinki, 1918-1920. Arabia: Riddle story; Greece: Riddle story.

Abbott, G. F. *Macedonian Folklore.* Cambridge, 1903.   Greece

Árnason, Jon. *Íslenzkar gátur.* Copenhagen, 1887.   Iceland

Arnaudov, M. P. *Bulgarski poslovitzi i gatanki.* Sofia, 1949. Bulgaria

Baissac, Charles. *Le Folklore de l'Ile Maurice.* Les Littératures populaires de toutes les nations, XXVII. Paris, 1888. Mauritius

Baring-Gould, S. "Yorkshire Household Riddles," *Notes and Queries,* 3rd ser. VIII (1865), 325.   England

Beauregard, G. M. O. "Devinettes malayses," *Revue des traditions populaires,* III (1888), 662-663; V (1890), 722-724. Malaya

Beckwith, Martha W. "Hawaiian Riddling," *American Anthropologist,* XXIV (1922), 311-331.   Hawaii

————. *Jamaica Anansi Stories,* Memoirs of the American Folklore Society, XVII. New York, 1924. British West Indies

Bernheisel, C. F. "Korean Conundrums," *Korean Review,* V (1905), 81-87; VI (1906), 59-62.   Korea

Bezerra, Alcides. "Adivinhas," in *Antologia do folclore brasileiro* (Luiz da Cámara Cascudo, Editor). São Paulo, n.d. Brazil

Bleakney, F. S. "Folklore from Ottawa and Vicinity," *Journal of American Folklore,* XXXI (1918), 169. Canada

Bodding, P. O. "Santal Riddles," *Oslo Etnografiske Museums Skrifter,* Bind 3, Heft 5 (1940), 209-256. India

The Booke of Meery Riddles. London, 1629. Reprinted in J. O. Halliwell-Phillips' *Literature of the 16th and 17th Centuries.* London, 1851.   England

Braga, Theophilo. *O povo portuguez.* V. II. Lisbon, 1885. Portugal

Brewster, Paul G. "Riddles from Southern Indiana," *Southern Folklore Quarterly,* III (1939), 93-105. United States

Brox, Arthur. "Gaater fraa Ytre Senja," *Norsk folkekultur,* XIII (1927), 15-29.   Norway

Brzoska, Kurt. *Das kleine Rätselbuch.* Darmstadt, 1951. Germany

Burne, Charlotte S. *Shropshire Folk-Lore.* London, 1883. England

Carter, Isabel. "White Mountain Riddles," *Journal of American Folklore,* XLVII (1934), 76-80. United States

Chambers, Robert. *Popular Rhymes of Scotland.* London, 1870. Scotland

Chappell, J. W. "Riddle Me, Riddle Me, Ree," *Folk-Say,* II (1930), 228-238.   United States

Colson, O. "Devinettes populaires aux pays wallon," *Revue des traditions populaires,* VII (1892), 147-153. Belgium

Dido, A. "Devinettes estoniennes," *Ibid.,* IX (1894), 32-36. Estonia

Dumoutier, Gustave. *Les Chants et traditions populaires des Annamites.* Collection de contes et chansons populaires, XV. Paris, 1890. Annam

Eben-Shosan, A., and I. Back. *Achuda-Na.* Jerusalem, 1944.   Israel
Farr, T. J. "Riddles and Superstitions of Middle Tennessee," *Journal of American Folklore,* XLVIII (1935), 318-326.   United States
Fauset, A. H. *Folklore from Nova Scotia.* Memoirs of the American Folklore Society, XXIV. New York, 1931.   Canada
————. "Negro Folk-Tales from the South," *Journal of American Folklore,* XL (1927), 276-292.   United States
Federowski, Michal. *Lud Bialoruski na Rusi Litewskiej,* V. IV. Towarzystwo Naukowe Warszawskie. Prace Etnologiczne V.I. Warsaw, 1935.   Russia
Feifalik, Julius. "Ein Hundert Volks- und Kinderräthsel aus Mähren," *Zeitschrift für deutsche Mythologie,* IV (1859), 367-384.   Czechoslovakia
Ferrand, Gabriel. *Contes populaires malgaches.* Collection de contes et chansons populaires, XIX. Paris, 1893.   Madagascar
Findlay, Wm. "Riddles," *Miscellanies of the Rymour Club,* I (Edinburgh, 1906-1911), 58-60.   Scotland
Fison, Lorimer. "On Fijian Riddles," *Journal of the Anthropological Institute of Great Britain and Ireland,* XI (1882), 406-410.   Fiji Islands
Flores, Eliodor. "Adivinanzas corrientes in Chile," *Revista de folklore chileno,* II (1911), iv and vii, 137-334.   Chile
Gardner, E. E. *Folklore from the Schoharie Hills.* Ann Arbor, 1937.   United States
Gaster, Moses. *The Exempla of the Rabbis.* London, 1924. Israel: Riddle story.
Giacobetti, A. *Recueil d'énigmes arabes.* Algiers, 1916.   Algeria
Gloger, Z. "Zagadki," *Encyklopedja Staropolska* V. IV, 473-478. Warsaw, 1903.   Poland
Gomes, Antonio Osmar. "Tradicões populares colhidas no baixo São Francisco." *Anais,* II, Primeiro Congresso Brasileiro de Folclore. Rio de Janeiro, 1951.   Brazil
Gorovei, Artur. "Devinettes populaires romaines," *Revue des traditions populaires,* VII (1892), 505-506; XII (1897), 22-34; XIII (1898), 113-119.   Rumania
Green, Edward. "Riddles from South Antrim," *Béaloideas,* XI (1941), 178-182.   Ireland
Greenleaf, Elisabeth B. "Riddles of Newfoundland," *The Marshall Review,* I (1938), 5-20.   Canada
Gregor, Walter. *Notes on the Folk-Lore of the North-East of Scotland.* Publications of the Folk-Lore Society, VII, London, 1881. Scotland
Grimms Household Tales (tr. Margaret Hunt). Vol II, 230. London, 1884. Germany: Riddle story.
Gutch, Eliza, and Mabel Peacock. *Examples of Printed Folk-Lore Concerning Lincolnshire.* Publications of the Folk-Lore Society, LXIX. London, 1908.   England

Guttman, Bruno. "Zur Psychologie des Dschaggarätsels," *Zeitschrift für Etnologie*, XLIII (1911), 522-540.   Africa
Halliwell-Phillips, J. O. *Nursery Rhymes of England.* London, 1886.
                                                                   England
————. *Popular Rhymes and Nursery Tales.* London, 1849.   England
Hahn, J. G. von. *Albanesische Studien.* Jena, 1854.   Albania
Hall, Robert A., Jr. *Haitian Creole: Grammar, Texts, Vocabulary.* American Anthropologist, LV, Memoir No. 74, Menasha, Wisconsin, 1953.
                                                                     Haiti
Halpert, Herbert. "Riddles from West Tennessee," *Hoosier Folklore Bulletin*, XVIII (1952), 29-42.   United States
Harries, Lyndon. "Some Riddles of the Maqua Peoples," *African Studies*, I, no. 4 (1942), 275-291.   Africa
Harris, H. G. *Hausa Stories and Riddles.* Weston-super-Mare, 1908.
                                                                   Africa
Heider, E., "Samoanische Rätsel . . .," *Archiv für Anthropologie*, XLII (1915), 119-137.   Samoa
Henssen, Gottfried. "Finnische Volksrätsel," *Zeitschrift des Vereins für Volkskunde*, XLIII (1933), 47-81.   Finland
Hollis, A. C. *The Nandi: Their Language and Folklore.* Oxford, 1909.
                                                                   Africa
Hudson, A. P. *Specimens of Mississippi Folklore.* Ann Arbor, 1928.
                                                            United States
Hull, Vernam E., and Archer Taylor. "A Collection of Welsh Riddles," *University of California Publications in Modern Philology*, XXVI (1942), 225-326.   Wales
Hyatt, H. M. *Folklore from Adams County, Illinois.* Memoirs of the Anna Egan Hyatt Foundation. New York, 1935.   United States
Hyde, Douglas. *Beside the Fire.* London, 1890.   Ireland
Ionova, M. N., and M. I. Pugovkin. "Yakutskie zagadki," *Sovetskii Folklor*, Nos. 4-5, 243-250. Moscow, 1936.   Siberia: Yakut
Jetté, Julius. "Riddles of the Ten'a Indians," *Anthropos*, VIII (1913), 181-201, 630-651.   Canada: Dene Indians
Judd, H. P. *Hawaiian Proverbs and Riddles.* Bulletin of the Bernice P. Bishop Museum, LXXVII. Honolulu, 1930.   Hawaii
Junod, H. P., and A. A. Jaques. *Vutlhari bya Vatonga. . . . The Wisdom of the Tonga-Shangaan People.* Cleveland, Transvaal, n.d.   Africa
Kamp, Jens. *Danske folkeminder, aeventur, gaader.* Odense, 1877.
                                                                 Denmark
Kershaw, N. *Stories and Ballads of the Far Past.* Cambridge, 1921. Iceland: Riddle story.
Knowles, J. H. "Kashmiri Riddles," *Journal of the Royal Asiatic Society of Bengal*, LVI (1887), 126-154.   India
Köhler, Reinhold (ed. J. Bolte). *Kleinere Schriften aus Märchenforschung*, Vol. I, 84 ff. Weimar, 1898. France: Riddle story.
Kuka, M. N. *The Wit and Humor of the Persians.* Bombay, 1894. Persia

Kvigstad, Just. *Lappische Sprichwörter und Rätsel.* Kristiania Etnografiska Museums Skrifter, I, No. 3. Oslo, 1922.   Lapland

Leather, Ella M. *The Folk-Lore of Herefordshire.* London, 1912. England

Lehmann-Nitsche, Robert. *Adivinanzas ríoplatenses.* Buenos Aires, 1911.
   Argentina; Paraguay

Littman, Enno. *Kairiner Sprichwörter und Rätsel.* Deutsche Morgenländische Gesellschaft. Leipzig, 1937.   Egypt

————. "Tigriña-Rätsel," *Zeitschrift der deutschen morgenländischen Gesellschaft,* XCII (1938), 611-632.   Abyssinia

Lullo, Orestes di. *El folklore de Santiago del Estero.* Tucumán, 1943.
   Argentina

Machado y Alvarez, Antonio (pseud.: Demófilo)'. *Colección de enigmas y adivinanzas....* Sevilla, 1880.   Spain

Mann, Oskar. *Persisch-kurdische Forschungen.* 2 V. Berlin, 1909-1910.
   Persia

Mason, J. A. "Porto Rican Riddles," *Journal of American Folklore,* XXIX (1916), 423-504.   Puerto Rico

Massip, Salvador. "Adivinanzas corrientes en Cuba," *Archivos del folklore cubano,* I (1925), 305-339.   Cuba

McCall, P. J. "Irish and Anglo-Irish Folklore Riddles," *Journal of the National Literary Society of Ireland,* I (1900), 61-80.   Ireland

Mitra, Sarat Chandra. "Bihari Life in Bihari Riddles," *Journal of the Anthropological Society of Bombay,* VII (1904-1907), 21-50. India: Riddle story.

————. "Riddles Current in the District of Chittagong in Eastern Bengal," *Ibid.,* XI (1917-1920), 296-327, 960-979; XIII (1924-1928), 657-672.   India

————. "Tibetan Folklore from Kalimpong in the District of Darjeeling in Eastern Himalayas," *Ibid.,* XIV (1927-1931), 465-466.   Tibet

Munshi, R. N. "A Few Parsee Riddles," *Ibid.,* X (1910), 94-100, 409-425.   India

Noguera, Eduardo Guadelupe. "Adivinanzas recogidas en México," *Journal of American Folklore,* XXXI (1918), 537-540.   Mexico

Opie, Iona and Peter. *The Oxford Dictionary of Nursery Rhymes.* Oxford, 1951.   England

Parsons, Elsie Clews. "Barbados Folklore," *Journal of American Folklore,* XXXVIII (1925), 276-292.   British West Indies

————. *Folklore from the Cape Verde Islands.* Memoirs of the American Folklore Society, XV, ii, Cambridge, Mass., 1923.
   Cape Verde Islands

————. *Folklore of the Antilles, French and English. Ibid.,* XXVI, iii, New York, 1943.   Haiti; British West Indies

————. "Spirituals and Other Folklore from the Bahamas," *Journal of American Folklore,* XLI (1928), 471-485.   British West Indies

Pauer, Paul Siliceo. "Adivinanzas recogidas en México," *Journal of American Folklore,* XXXI (1918), 541.   Mexico

Pedersen, Holger. *Zur albanesische Volkskunde.* Copenhagen, 1898.
Albania

Perera, A. A. *Sinhalese Folklore Notes.* Bombay, 1917.   Ceylon

Petrov, A. "Lud ziemi dobrzynskiej," *Zbior wiadomosci do Antropologji Krajowej,* II, pt. 3 (1872), 178-182.   Poland

Phillott, D. C. "Some Riddles Collected from Dervishes in the South of Persia," *Journal of the Royal Asiatic Society of Bengal,* n.s., II (1906), 83-93. Persian Dervishes.

Pires, A. T. "Adivinhas portuguezas . . . do Alemtejo," *Archivio,* III (1884), 113-120.   Portugal

————. "Adivinhas portuguezas. . . do Douro," *Ibid.,* VIII (1889), 93-96.   Portugal

Pitrè, Giuseppe. *Indovinelli, dubbi, scioglilingua del popolo siciliano.* Biblioteca delle tradizioni popolari siciliani, XX. Turin, 1897.   Italy

Praeger, S. Rosamond. "Riddles from County Down," *Béaloideas,* IV (1933-34), 144-146.   Ireland

Quijada Jara, Sergio. *Estampas Huancavelicas.* Lima, 1944.   Peru

Randolph, Vance, and Mary Celestia Parler. "Riddles from Arkansas," *Journal of American Folklore,* LXVII (1954), 253-259.
United States

Randolph, Vance, and Isabel Spradley. "Ozark Mountain Riddles," *Ibid.,* XLVII (1934), 81-89.   United States

Randolph, Vance, and Archer Taylor. "Riddles in the Ozarks," *Southern Folklore Quarterly,* VI (1944), 1-10.   United States

Redfield, Margaret Park. *The Folk Literature of a Yucatecan Town.* Contributions to American Ethnology, III, No. 13. Washington, 1937.   Mexico

Revue des traditions populaires, V (1890), passim.   France

Richter, Friedrich. *Raten und Denken.* Hamburg, 1943.   Germany

Rolland, Eugene. *Devinettes ou énigmes populaires de la France suivies . . . d'un recueil de 77 indovinelli publié à Trévise en 1628. . . . préface de Gaston Paris.* Paris, 1877.   France; Italy

Rorie, David. "Some Old Scottish Rhyming Riddles," *Scots Magazine,* n.s., XXIII (1935), 148-154.   Scotland

Rudolph, R. C. "The Riddle in China," *California Folklore Quarterly,* I (1942), 65-82.   China

Sadovnikov, D. N. *Zagadki russkogo naroda.* St. Petersburg, 1875.
Russia

Sampson, John. "Fifty Welsh Gypsy Folk-Riddles," *Journal of the Gypsy-Lore Society,* n.s., V (1911-1912), 241-254.   Welsh Gypsy.

Schapera, Isaac. "Kxatla Riddles and Their Significance," *Bantu Studies,* VI (1932), 215-231.   Africa

Schleicher, August. *Litauische Märchen, Sprichworte, Rätsel und Lieder.* Weimar, 1857.   Lithuania

Schwab, George. *Tribes of the Liberian Hinterland.* Papers of the Peabody Museum, Harvard University, XXXI. Cambridge, Mass., 1947.   Africa

Sibree, James. "Folk-Tales of the Malagasy, II, Riddles and Conundrums," *Folk-Lore Journal*, I (1883), 38-40. Madagascar
Stafset, K. D. *280 Gamle norske gaator*. Velden, 1908. Norway
Starr, Frederick. "Japanese Riddles," *Transactions of the Asiatic Society of Japan*, XXXVIII (1910), 1-49. Japan
————. *A Little Book of Filipino Riddles*. Yonkers, 1909.
Philippine Islands
Stoilov, Kh. P. "Klasifikatziya na bulgarskite narodni gatanki," *Sbornik za narodni umotvoreniya i narodopis*, XXX (1914), 1-146. Bulgaria
Stokes, Whitley. "Irish Riddles," *Celtic Review*, I (1904), 132-135.
Ireland
Ström, Fredrik. *Svenska folkgåtor*. Stockholm, 1937. Sweden
Tafel, Albert. *Meine Tibetreise*. Stuttgart, 1914. Tibet
Tammi, Ernesto. "Indovinelli piacentini," *Il folklore italiano*, V (1930), 179-185. Italy
Taylor, Archer. "American Indian Riddles," *Journal of American Folklore*, LVII (1944), 1-14. United States (Arapaho Indian)
————. *An Annotated Collection of Mongolian Riddles*. Transactions of the American Philosophical Society, n.s., V. 44, Pt. 3. Philadelphia, 1954. Mongolia
————. *English Riddles from Oral Tradition*. Berkeley, 1951. Holland; Java; Hungary; Greece. See Acknowledgments.
Tschiedel, J. "Italienische Volksrätsel," *Zeitschrift des Vereins für Volkskunde*, VI (1896), 276-283. Italy
Vukovic, M. *Sbirka zagonetaka*. Zagreb, 1890. Yugoslavia
Waugh, F. W. "Canadian Folklore from Ontario," *Journal of American Folklore*, XXXI (1918), 63-72. Canada
Wheeler, Howard T. *Tales from Jalisco, Mexico*. Memoirs of the American Folklore Society, XXXV. Philadelphia, 1943. Mexico: Riddle story.
Wichmann, Y. "Wotjakische Sprachproben, II, Sprichwörter, Rätsel, Märchen, Sagen," *Journal de la Société finno-ougrienne*, XIX (1901), 10-51. Russia (Votiak)
Weidemann, F. J. *Aus dem inneren und äusseren Leben der Ehsten*. St. Petersburg, 1876. Estonia
Wintemberg, W. J., and Katherine H. Wintemberg. "Folklore from Grey County, Ontario," *Journal of American Folklore*, XXXI (1918), 123-124. Canada
Wlislocki, Heinrich von. *Volksdichtungen der siebenbürgischen und südungarischen Zigeuner*. Vienna, 1890. Hungarian Gypsies.
Wright, Elizabeth M. *Rustic Speech and Folk-Lore*. London, 1913.
England
Zahler, H. "Rätsel aus Münchenbuchsee," *Schweizerisches Archiv für Volkskunde*, IX (1905), 81-111, 187-210. Switzerland
Zow, Lise. "Riddles from China," *New York Times Magazine*, December 2, 1945. China

NORTH
PACIFIC
OCEAN

NORTH
ATLANTIC
OCEAN

SOUTH
ATLANTIC
OCEAN

N
W   E
S